STATISTICS, SCIENCE AND PUBLIC POLICY

IV. THE TWO CULTURES?

STATISTICS, SCIENCE AND PUBLIC POLICY

IV. THE TWO CULTURES?

Proceedings of the Conference on
Statistics, Science and Public Policy
held at Herstmonceux Castle, Hailsham, U.K.
April 21-24, 1999

A.M. HERZBERG *and* I. KRUPKA *Editors*

Canadian Cataloguing in Publication Data

Conference on Statistics, Science and Public Policy (4th : 1999 :
Hailsham, England)
    Statistics, science and public policy IV : the two cultures?
proceedings of the Conference on Statistics, Science and Public Policy held at
Herstmonceux Castle, Hailsham, U.K., April 21-24, 1999

Includes bibliographical references.
ISBN 0-88911-920-1

1. Science and state – Congresses. I. Herzberg, A. M. II. Krupka, I. (Ivo).
III. Title.

Q124.6.C665 1999   338.9'26   C00-930587-4

Cover by Graphic Design: Peter Dorn

Photograph of Herstmonceux Castle courtesy of Dee Padfield

Photograph of Gerhard Herzberg taken by John Reeves

Table of Contents

Part IV: NATURAL AND SOCIAL SCIENCES

Part V: SCIENCE AND PUBLIC POLICY

Part VI: THE CULTURES OF ACCOUNTABILITY

In Memoriam

GERHARD HERZBERG, P.C., C.C., F.R.S.C., F.R.S.
December 25, 1904 to March 3, 1999

In Memoriam

These conferences might never have taken place without the influence of Dr. Gerhard Herzberg, a Canadian physicist and Nobel laureate, who spent his life in the pursuit of science, but also loved and found time for the arts, especially music. He was an accomplished singer.

Born on Christmas Day in 1904 in Hamburg, Germany, Gerhard Herzberg had early on wanted to be an astronomer, but this was not possible as he lacked private means. He was also interested in physics and managed to obtain a private scholarship for the first two years at the Technical University in Darmstadt. Over the following years, he received public funding. After his graduation from the Technical University with a doctorate in engineering, he held post-doctorate fellowships at the University of Göttingen and the University of Bristol. He then returned to the Technical University in Darmstadt.

In 1933, Dr. J.W.T. Spinks, a young chemistry professor at the University of Saskatchewan, came to Darmstadt to spend a year working with Dr. Herzberg. Because the political situation in Germany was deteriorating, Dr. Spinks managed, with the help of the President of the University of Saskatchewan, to obtain a position for Dr. Herzberg at the University; the Carnegie Foundation of New York provided the initial funding. Dr. Herzberg said that his experiences at the University of Saskatchewan and in Saskatoon, from 1935 to 1945, were the best ten years of his life. From that time, he identified himself as a Canadian.

After three years at the Yerkes Observatory of the University of Chicago in Williams Bay, Wisconsin, Dr. Herzberg returned to Canada in 1948 to the National Research Council of Canada. He was appointed

Director of the Division of Physics in 1949 and retired from that position in 1969. He remained at the Council as Distinguished Research Scientist and continued his research for almost the next thirty years until illness intervened.

Dr. Herzberg was awarded many honours, including the Nobel Prize for Chemistry in 1971. He never forgot the University of Saskatchewan:

> It is obvious that the work that has earned me the Nobel Prize was not done without a great deal of help. First of all, while at the University of Saskatchewan, I had the full and understanding support of successive Presidents and of the Faculty of the University who, under very stringent conditions, did their utmost to make it possible for me to proceed with my scientific work.

Before becoming the Director of the Division of Physics at the National Research Council, he was told that his "main administrative function would be to find first-class people for the positions that were open and let them use their own judgement in selecting their own research projects rather than try to direct them."

Dr. Herzberg believed that advances in science stem from research done when individuals are given free rein and not restricted by the policy decisions of government agencies or committees. Demonstrating his conviction that administrators are meant to support science, Dr. Herzberg wore a white laboratory coat even when confined to his desk. The key to scientific success and technological advance, he felt, was in the laboratory, not in the office or committee room.

He defended publicly his opinion that a society should maintain a high standard in science and the arts; survival should not be society's only goal. He held that all citizens needed to consider "the works of art, literature, and basic science as not merely the icing on the cake but as the essence of human existence."

Dr. Herzberg's advice, his science, his work on behalf of dissidents, his campaigns for the funding of pure science by government and his sense of fun will always be remembered through these conferences and proceedings. They are his legacy.

Foreword

These proceedings summarize the sessions of the "Conference on Statistics, Science and Public Policy: The Two Cultures?" held at Herstmonceux Castle in the United Kingdom, April 21 to 24, 1999. This was the fourth conference in the series Statistics, Science and Public Policy.

Since the conference was aimed at promoting dialogue, participants who made presentations were free to choose their format. Some gave formal papers, others were more informal, and one or two spoke extemporaneously, adjusting their remarks in the light of themes explored by previous speakers and discussions. The papers and speeches have been edited or summarized for publication by the authors, editors or both.

A.M. Herzberg
I. Krupka
February 2000

Acknowledgements

This conference would not have taken place without the assistance of many. Professors Sir David Cox, F.K. Hare, J. Meisel and A.T. Stewart; P. Milliken, Member of Parliament for Kingston and the Islands and Deputy Speaker of the Canadian House of Commons supplied advice and ideas. A. Morgan provided constant reassurance and J. Zakos considerable skills.

Support from Queen's University came through the kind offices of the Vice-Principals, Advancement, Research and Academic; the Dean of Arts; and the Head of the Department of Mathematics and Statistics. This included funding as well as the services of H. Bennett and J. Whittle.

The financial and in-kind contributions of the following: Air Canada; Berry Brothers and Rudd, Ltd.; Camera Kingston; Campus Bookstore, Queen's University; the Donner Canadian Foundation; Galerie d'Art Vincent, Château Laurier, Ottawa; the Geological Survey of Canada; GlaxoWellcome, U.K.; and a number of anonymous donors are much appreciated.

The excellent editorial skills of M. Banting and S. Fraser and the fine production work of M. Howes and V. Jarus of the Publications Unit of the School of Policy Studies, Queen's University, are acknowledged.

Dr. A.M. Benidickson, Chancellor-Emeritus of Queen's University, participated in the conference and brought great style to the occasion.

Contributors

E.B. Andersen, University of Copenhagen

J.C. Bailar, III, University of Chicago

T.A. Brzustowski, Natural Sciences and Engineering Research Council of Canada

P. Calamai, *The Toronto Star*

P. Campbell, *Nature*

A.J. Carty, National Research Council of Canada

Sir David Cox, Nuffield College, Oxford

T.G. Flynn, Queen's University

C.E.S. Franks, Queen's University

F.D. Gault, Statistics Canada

E.A. Gehan, Georgetown University Medical Center

F.K. Hare, University of Toronto

A.M. Herzberg, Queen's University

L. Horlick, University of Saskatchewan

P.O. Larsen, The Danish National Research Foundation

D.B. McLay, Queen's University

J. Meisel, Queen's University

P. Milliken, Member of Parliament, Canada

R.W. Oldford, University of Waterloo

G.H. Reynolds, Centers for Disease Control and Prevention, Atlanta

S. Strauss, *The Globe and Mail*

R.E. Taylor, Stanford Linear Accelerator Center

M.E. Thompson, University of Waterloo

L. Wolpert, University College London

PART I

INTRODUCTION

CHAPTER 1

The Two Cultures?

A.M. Herzberg

The idea for these conferences arose out of many continuing issues: the lack of communication among statisticians and scientists, the difficulty and inaccuracy in communicating scientific results to the public through the media, the recent interest in the support of science from the public purse, and whether science should be directed by government. The purpose of the first conference was to bring together different disciplines in order for people to get to know each other. This might then lead to influencing governments to increase their support of science and the arts. Now, although this is still an aim of the conferences, they have become more of a format for discussions and collegiality on a wide range of topics. A Chinese philosopher once said "Of a good leader who talks little, when his work is done and his aim fulfilled, [people] will say 'we did it ourselves'."

What is meant by "The Two Cultures"? Why is this our sub-title this year? It is forty years since C.P. Snow published his book *The Two Cultures*, and fifty-five years since President Franklin Roosevelt asked Vanevar Bush for advice on the organization of and support for scientific research. Bush's report, titled *Science: The Endless Frontier*, was published in 1945. Once the title for this conference was decided upon, I found that there seemed to be not two cultures but perhaps a countable number of different cultures. The question of where the boundaries between the cultures are also arose.

There are many cultures or dichotomies between the two cultures. Snow said that he meant by culture "intellectual development, development of the mind" (1965, p. 62) and "a group of persons living in the same environment, linked by common habits, common assumptions, a common way of life" (ibid., p. 64). The two cultures for Snow were the literary intellectuals, including the humanities and social scientists, and the scientists.

However, the chasm between his two cultures is part of the reason these conferences began. It may be possible to remove the chasm and move to one culture, but there may be now a "double standard" between these two cultures. On the one hand, everyone is expected to read and understand literature, including the works of obscure writers, but not necessarily to know how to make the most elementary calculations. Further, scientists who do basic research have their work directed by governments, etc., but benefactors of the arts do not necessarily make those demands. Professor Meisel remarked at the second conference:

> two communities which should work together closely but who often are distant and even estranged need to be persuaded to collaborate better. A bridge will have to be built from the science universe to that of decision makers — officials, politicians and the public. For this to happen, efforts must be initiated by both sides (Meisel, 1998, p. 150).

"The late Professor E.A. Milne [the famous theoretical physicist] often said that adults with their prejudices and preconceptions might put things upside down and that it is only children with their open minds who can see things right-side up" (Cox and Herzberg, 1972). By looking at the world through the eyes of a different culture, one might understand various situations better. The late Isaiah Berlin wrote of the two cultures of the hedgehog and the fox types which are seen everywhere: the fox knows many things but the hedgehog knows only one thing well (Berlin, 1978).

Where do the two cultures of nature and architecture meet? Architecture sometimes tries to mimic nature. J.B. Jackson wrote that man-made complexes were sometimes an imitation of landscapes; "at their best they provide us with something of the stimulation we get from a brief walk through a valley among trees and open fields; they satisfy for the time being our craving for contact with a variety of forms and spaces and lights and sounds" (Jackson, 1970, p. 83). He produces a vivid and thought-provoking description of New York's Grand Central Station. Many cultures flow into each other and try to emulate each other.

Allan Bromley's recent remarks about science and the law sum up the situation for many pairs of cultures in this day and age:

In the early days, it might have been possible for science and the law to have remained in splendid isolation, but in today's increasingly technological society, science, technology, and the law are inexorably drawn together. And the time has surely come when we need to better understand one another and how we work (Bromley, 1999, p. 110).

In his "second look" at the two cultures in 1965, Snow wrote: "It is dangerous to have two cultures which can't or don't communicate. In a time when science is determining much of our destiny, that is, whether we live or die, it is dangerous in the most practical terms" (Snow, 1965, p. 98).

At the conference, various cultures were discussed, including the culture of the media, which sometimes inflates items out of all proportion, and the culture of accountability which can cost more than is spent on the original outcome. Professor W.K. Hayman of Imperial College, London, recently pointed out that the invasive and expensive procedure of accountability is like the gardener who keeps pulling up the plants to see if they are still growing. It may also be caused by the appointment of non-scientists and non-academics as the heads of scientific institutes and universities, etc.

Charles Percy Snow was born on October 15, 1905 and died on July 1, 1980 at the age of 74. He was as he, himself, has said: "By training ... a scientist: by vocation ... a writer" (Snow, 1971, p. 13). Snow is well-known for his "epic" novel *Strangers and Brothers*. His essay "The Two Cultures and the Scientific Revolution" was the Rede Lecture given in Cambridge and appeared first in the June and July 1959 issues of *Encounter* (Snow, 1959a, b).

In the August 1959 issue of *Encounter*, many luminaries wrote letters about this paper. Bertrand Russell wrote:

I have been reading your Rede Lecture with very great interest and as much pleasure as the subject-matter permitted. All that you say as to what ought to be done commands my assent. The separation between science and culture is very much greater than it used to be. In the time of Charles II [1630-85] it did not exist, and in the early nineteenth century there were still many bridges from one territory to the other. Cartwright, who invented the power-loom, was my grandfather's tutor and taught him to construe the odes of Horace. So far as I have been able to discover, his invention of the power-loom remained unknown to my grandfather (Russell, 1959).

Of course, Russell was also well experienced in both the science and humanities worlds.

G.H. Bantock also wrote of Snow's papers:

> The main point of Sir Charles's argument, however, is that this division between literary intellectuals and scientists, 'this polarization is sheer loss to us all'.... He thinks that there are creative possibilities when two subjects or disciplines cross-fertilize or in some way stimulate or rub up against each other ....

> I have a good deal of sympathy with this view of loss sustained. Certainly writers too easily sneer at 'illiterate' scientists without appreciating their own ignorance of what precisely it is to pursue the intellectual adventure of science. They have not been ready, as Wordsworth thought they should, to carry 'sensation into the midst of the objects of ... science itself' (Bantock, 1959, p. 427).

C.P. Snow re-published his Rede Lectures in a small edition called *The Two Cultures and A Second Look: An expanded version of the two cultures and the scientific revolution* in 1965. The preface to this edition written in 1963 states:

> Since the original lecture has been written about a good deal, I have thought it best to leave it as it was first printed, apart from the correction of two small inaccuracies.

> In the second part, as I explain, I have looked at the lecture again in the light of various comments and the passage of four years (Snow, 1965, p. iv).

In a paper entitled "Remarks on the Boundaries of Knowledge", my father, Gerhard Herzberg, was concerned not only with the frontiers but also with the limitations of knowledge. After a discussion on the boundaries of knowledge that are intrinsic to the nature of the physical universe, including space travel to the moon which was once thought to have been impossible, he considered the boundaries that are introduced by the human mind. He noted that:

> The limitations to the advance of knowledge that are introduced by the limited extent of our memory (and I realize that there are many other reasons) are illustrated by the sharp schism between literary intellectuals on the one hand and natural scientists on the other, so eloquently described by C.P. Snow in his little book *The Two Cultures and the Scientific Revolution*. Of course, this schism really goes much further, as was recognized by C.P. Snow; even among scientists of one discipline there is

considerable lack of understanding of the work in other disciplines. While much of this schism is caused by the limitations of the average intellect, the division is further fostered to a considerable degree by our educational system, which in my opinion gives far too much choice to students of our high schools. I recently came across a statement by Arnold Toynbee which illustrates this point. He said: "Looking back, I now regret that, at the age of sixteen, at school, I was allowed to choose between starting on calculus and giving up mathematics altogether in order to spend the whole of my working time on reading more widely in the Greek and Latin classics. I ought not to have been given this choice at that age. I chose wrong, and consequently the field of mathematics, and the branches of science founded on mathematics, has been closed to me."

... let us develop a cultural climate which believes that human excellence is a good thing in itself, a climate in which all members of society can rejoice and delight in the things that the small number of exceptional members is able to do, without asking what use they have for survival. We must come to the point where even the average citizen considers the works of art, literature, and basic science as not merely the icing on the cake but as the essence of human existence. Without that, to quote C.P. Snow, 'some of the major hopes, the major glories of the human race will rapidly disappear.'

My father ends by saying:

the striving for excellence in order to increase our cultural heritage and to extend the frontiers of knowledge is the most important aim of mankind. There may be more urgent things to be done in connection with our survival. But we must not let these necessities detract us entirely from our devotion to the striving for knowledge for its own sake, to the aim of understanding man and his world (Herzberg, 1974).

Vannevar Bush was born on March 11, 1890 and died on June 30, 1974. In 1964 he wrote: "no science worthy of the name is so pure as to be entirely devoid of possibilities of service to the needs of a complex civilization" (Zachary, 1997, p. 35). By the age of 57, he personified military research in America and was the most politically powerful inventor in America since Benjamin Franklin. Bush was an engineer and an inventor. In 1933, anticipating C.P. Snow, Bush said in a testimonial to Elihu Thomson, a distinguished inventor and entrepreneur on the occasion of Thomson's eightieth birthday:

You have showed [sic] us that a man may be truly a professor and at the same time very practical.... You have shown us that a scientist or engineer may be, even in this complex modern world, versatile and yet not superficial.... In these days, when there is a tendency to specialize so closely, it is well for us to be reminded that the possibilities of being at once broad and deep did not pass with Leonardo da Vinci or even Benjamin Franklin. Men of our profession — we teachers — are bound to be impressed with the tendency of youths of strikingly capable minds to become interested in one small corner of science and uninterested in the rest of the world. We can pass by those who, through mental laziness, prefer to be superficially and casually interested in everything. But it is unfortunate when a brilliant and creative mind insists upon living in a modern monastic cell. We feel the results of this tendency keenly, as we find men of affairs wholly untouched by the culture of modern science, and scientists without the leavening of humanities. One most unfortunate product is the type of engineer who does not realize that in order to apply the fruits of science for the benefit of mankind, he must not only grasp the principles of science, but must also know the needs and aspirations, the possibilities and the frailties, of those whom he would serve (Bush, 1933, p. 419).

When Bush was asked formally by Franklin Roosevelt to write a report on the situation of postwar scientific research, and thoughts for the future, he wrote *Science: The Endless Frontier* which "skillfully [sic] equated scientific and technical progress with the national health — and convincingly made the argument that government must finance independent researchers at levels far above those seen before the war" (Zachary, 1997, p. 3). Roosevelt had written in his letter of November 7, 1944: "New frontiers of the mind are before us, and if they are pioneered with the same vision, boldness, and drive with which we have waged this war we can create a fuller and more fruitful employment and a fuller and more fruitful life." The report was submitted to President Truman. Bush felt at the time that "a few scientists sitting as chiefs of regular [federal] departments would make quite a difference" (ibid., p. 256).

The new 1998 United States science report *Unlocking Our Future* was not a report guided by one man as before because, rightly or wrongly, it is necessary today to have input from many (what we might term) cultures or "interested parties"! The study was conducted by Representative Vernon Ehlers, Vice-Chairman of the House Committee on Science. The committee was asked by the Speaker of the United States House of Representatives to undertake a study of the "current state of the Nation's science and technology policies" and to outline a "framework for an updated national science policy that can serve as a policy guide to the Committee, Congress and the Nation." The report went on to recommend substantial funding for basic (or fundamental) research across science, mathematics and engineering; see Block and Vest (1999).

In 1971, C.P. Snow (1971, p. 224) became much more pessimistic about the situation, and at the end of his epilogue, he saw the young as saviours. Can we say the same today, twenty-eight years later or forty years after the original article?

In summary, the words my father said some time ago are appropriate not only for Canada, but all countries:

> A high standard of living is not, as such, a goal worth striving for unless a high standard of living includes a high standard of art, literature and science.... If Canada is to be economically prosperous without at the same time supporting the arts and sciences for their own sakes, it will not reach the level of a great nation (quoted in Karsh, 1978, p. 72).

REFERENCES

Bantock, G.H. (1959), "A Scream of Horror: Reaction to the Widening Gap Between Literature and Science", *The Listener*, September 17, pp. 427-428.

Berlin, I. (1978), *The Hedgehog and the Fox. An Essay on Tolstoy's View of History*, Chicago: Elephant Paperbacks.

Block, E. and Vest, C.M. (1999), "Congress and U.S. Research" (Editorial), *Science* 283:1639.

Bromley, D.A. (1999), "Science and the Law", in *AAAS Science and Technology Policy Yearbook 1999*, ed. A.H. Teich, S.D. Nelson, C. McEnaney and T.M. Drake, Washington, D.C.: American Association for the Advancement of Science, pp. 109-119.

Bush, V. (1933), "In Honour of Professor Elihu Thomson", *Science* 77:418-420.

_____ (1945), *Science. The Endless Frontier. A Report to the President*, Washington, D.C.: United States Government Printing Office.

Cox, D.R. and Herzberg, A.M. (1972), "On a Statistical Problem of E.A. Milne", With a historical introduction by S. Chandrasekhar, *Proceedings of the Royal Society of London*, A331:273-283.

Herzberg, G. (1974), "Remarks on the Boundaries of Knowledge", *Transactions of the Royal Society of Canada Series* IV(12):21-29.

Jackson, J.B. (1970), *Landscapes: Selected Writings of J.B. Jackson*, ed. E.H. Zube, Amherst, MA: The University of Massachusetts Press.

Karsh, Y. (1978), *Karsh Canadians*, Toronto: University of Toronto Press.

Meisel, J. (1998), "Toward Finding Solutions", in *Statistics, Science and Public Policy II. Hazards and Risks*, ed. A.M. Herzberg and I. Krupka, Kingston, Ont.: Queen's University, pp. 147-151.

Russell, B (1959), "The 'Two Cultures' Snobbery", *Encounter* 13:71.

Snow, C.P. (1959a), "The Two Cultures and the Scientific Revolution", *Encounter* 12:17-24.

_____ (1959b), "The Two Cultures and the Scientific Revolution", *Encounter* 13:22-27.

_____ (1965), *The Two Cultures and a Second Look: An expanded version of the two cultures and the scientific revolution*, Cambridge: Cambridge University Press.

_____ (1971), *Public Affairs*, London: Macmillan.

Zachary, G.P. (1997), *Endless Frontier: Vannevar Bush, Engineer of the American Century*, New York: The Free Press.

CHAPTER 2

A Chasm of Incomprehension

P. Calamai

INTRODUCTION

Forty years ago, Charles Percy Snow delivered a talk at Cambridge University which set the scientific cat among the humanities pigeons. Snow did not speak long in the Rede Lecture, but what he had to say still echoes today. His central theme was that advanced Western societies had lost even the pretence of a shared culture. This fragmentation was leading us to interpret the past wrongly, misjudge the present and deny our hopes for the future.

Snow advanced four main arguments:

1. People educated in the arts and humanities generally felt they could get on perfectly well in life without the faintest understanding of something as fundamental as molecular biology, and said so regularly. Yet few scientists exalted in knowing nothing about Shakespeare or Dickens.
2. Public life was dominated by these intellectually undernourished non-scientists and, as a result, the natural sciences were generally poorly understood and misapplied in national and international affairs.
3. Schools should postpone the streaming of students into the study of science or the arts and, even after specialization, favour a more comprehensive curriculum.
4. The world would be a better place if natural scientists (and science) had much more say in the running of it — at least equal to the influence of non-scientists.

The first two items are empirical observations which were basically correct then, as they still are today, although perhaps a little bit less so. The third has been the object of much educational experimentation without any agreement on what works best.

The fourth proposition was the real battleground and many scientists still see it that way. Today, however, the relative positions have now reversed. Scientists are no longer primarily the outsiders, envious of the privileges of the literary classes. In universities and the corporate world, at least, it is the scientific culture that is dominant and the artistic culture that seeks the crumbs from the "High Table". And a similar reversal has happened in our mass culture. It is far more likely today that someone under the age of forty will have read *The Double Helix* than they will have *The Aeneid*, or at least be able to identify the story.

I do not believe this outcome would have delighted C.P. Snow. My understanding of his speech and other writings is that he was trying to be a peacemaker, to close the gap between the warring factions of humanities and sciences. Underpinning all his work is the assumption that nature needs to be understood through the sciences as well as through the arts and humanities. That is nature writ large — or, as Douglas Adams would say, *Life, the Universe and Everything*.

These various understandings of nature together produce a culture, a way of sharing with others our grasp of the world. In Snow's hopeful view, this cultural outreach was intended to help other nations to improve, first technologically, then materially and finally democratically — although the process was not seen as anything so deterministic or sequential. I am going to stay with the same theme as Snow, talking also about a chasm that threatens science and the arts. But a far more insidious one.

THE IDEA OF TWO CULTURES

Back in 1959, C.P. Snow managed to capture an emerging *zeitgeist*. His speech gave birth to a catch-phrase whose longevity rivals his other celebrated coinage, the "Corridors of Power". But the vast attention paid to "The Two Cultures" speech troubled Snow because he believed the concept had eclipsed two more important themes of the Rede Lecture: the urgent need to address the population explosion and the widening gap between rich and poor globally.

There is one very simple reason why the two cultures idea so captured the public fancy, Snow's anecdotal style and prose were more attuned to the Sunday supplement than to the seminar room. Academic critics attacked this popular approach as "vulgar" and unsuited to a scholarly debate. Perhaps subconsciously, many of these critics simply assumed there was no need to make the arguments entertaining or accessible. This issue was far too important to be left to ordinary people.

Ordinary people. In my view, this is where the two cultures issue has migrated today, shifting like one of those swirling vortexes of sea water that breaks away from an underwater vent to carry an entire column of marine life kilometres away. Four decades after C.P. Snow's lecture the most pressing cause for concern is the widening chasm of understanding between those in our societies who seek knowledge as part of their job, and everyone else. This chasm may be most obvious and dangerous in scientific areas but it affects all fields of advanced knowledge.

Right now would probably be a good time to stop and try to nail down some definitions. The first group will be called the professional knowledge-seekers. It would naturally include all university faculty who carry out continuing scholarly research plus the doctoral and postdoctoral levels, but not journalism and others in similar master-apprentice roles and not technologists. Outside academia, one would obviously want to include the research establishments, whether public or private, like the Sanger Centre at Cambridge, the Rice Research Institute in the Philippines, CERN (the European Organization for Nuclear Research), the Mayo Clinic, the National Research Council of Canada in Ottawa, and so on. Also add the research departments of corporations, think tanks of all stripes, and the public agencies that ensure the safety of our drugs and the purity of our air. Yet even with such a generous definition, this new academy is never going to amount to even one-tenth of the population in the most advanced societies, and elsewhere much less.

The Public and Scientific Information

Here is the issue. What these professional knowledge-seekers do, and *why* they do it, is steadily becoming more and more alien to the vast majority outside the knowledge academies. Partly that is because the knowledge-seekers are regularly falling into the trap of talking too much about things and not enough about ideas. This is understandable, given the pressures to secure funding and demonstrate social relevance. And I concede that journalists are all too guilty of just asking scientists "What is this good for?" rather than "How does this improve our understanding?" This overwhelming emphasis on imminent practical applications of knowledge-seeking creates a false picture, and one that is potentially damaging to public comprehension.

A much more immediate damage, however, arises from the fact that all too often those within the knowledge academies do not explain their work at all. And when one of their number becomes something of a media star, they risk being pilloried. Consider the flak which Jacob Bronowski took, or Carl Sagan, a scientific giant who was turned down for membership by the U.S. National Academy of Science.

Most scientists deal with this danger of ostracism by leaving all the explanations to science popularizers. This is either incredible naiveté or monumental disdain. Trying to delegate the job of explaining what science is all about to popularizers is not much better than putting a white coat and a stethoscope on an actor for a TV commercial about headache remedies. No one is fooled and the chance to provide a glimpse of a real scientist is squandered. This lack of communication and comprehension has been around for a long time. In *Science and Government* (1961), C.P. Snow wrote that a number of the most intelligent people in the world cannot really comprehend the nature, and fallibility, of scientific argument. A later commentator speaks about the paradox of respect without comprehension, a phrase that does a pretty good job of capturing the status of most scientists in Western nations in the second half of this century.

Up until now, scientists and others have been able to live with the irritant of this public incomprehension of science. It was irksome but far from debilitating, an itch that got scratched regularly at meetings like this one.

Yet the stakes today are too high to form mere scratching. Think of some current issues for which a well-informed public is desirable: genetically modified organisms, xenotransplantation, nuclear waste disposal, cultural nationalism, global climate change, early childhood education, drug abuse, new reproductive technology, gene swapping or add your own favourite from the groaning smorgasbord of issues.

On all of these complex issues, we need the best possible advice from our knowledge-seekers. For example, grasping the main elements of an issue like global climate change requires drawing on not only the natural sciences (like atmospheric chemistry, climatology, physical oceanography and so on), but also the social sciences (economics, psychology, geography) and the humanities (for insight into the human spirit, among many aspects). Yet increasingly, the vast majority of people are seeking insight on such issues from sources other than those in the best position to know: the public prefers a Website of unknown provenance over what their own government tells them when it comes to electromagnetic radiation. They turn to those whom Sagan catalogued in *The Demon-Haunted World*.

I think part of the reason for such seemingly illogical choices is a growing disenchantment with the formalized process of seeking knowledge, a rejection of the paradigms that scientists and other scholars have laboured so long to establish, and to cherish. This disenchantment brings with it a very real danger that society is not only losing the ability to draw insight from scientific advances and to evaluate science intelligently but also abandoning the desire to do so.

A Chasm of Incomprehension

I want to shine a first beam across this chasm of incomprehension, what C.P. Snow was fond of calling a "sighting shot". I am going to concentrate on the natural sciences but these arguments apply, *mutatis mutandis*, to the social sciences and the arts and humanities as well. Back in 1959, Snow's starting point was that the lack of understanding of science was imparting an unscientific flavour to Britain's culture; he feared this could all too easily become anti-scientific. Snow was correct about many things (he forecast the ascendancy of biology over physics, for example), but he was wrong about the anti-scientific backlash.

So my starting point is not an anti-science backlash, although that may yet come. Instead it is an alienation from both the fruits of science and technology and also from the process of science, and of intellectual endeavour generally. From whence does such alienation toward science spring? It is common to blame increasing specialization, which makes it impossible for even the best-educated individuals to understand what is happening outside their own niche. One particularly poignant example came to light in a *New York Times* interview with Martin Wells, a Cambridge zoologist who is one of the great experts on cephalopods, the grandson of H.G. Wells, and author of *Civilization and the Limpet*:

The sad thing now is that in my department here in Cambridge there is only a handful of us who probably can tell one animal from another. The rest are molecular biologists and model-makers.... My elder son is a veterinarian who has gone into molecular biology to do research into muscular dystrophy. When he and his wife are discussing his work, I practically can't understand them (Driefus, 1998).

With all respect to Martin Wells, I still cannot accept overspecialization as a satisfactory explanation for public alienation. Despite this fractionation at the laboratory-bench end, many branches of science are more unified at the conceptual end than ever before. All those facts are finally beginning to fit together. Maybe then it is the accelerated advance in scientific knowledge that is to blame. The Massachusetts Institute of Technology recently buried an Internet time capsule; they plan to dig it up in five years. In real life, however, there are knowledge-feedback loops to prompt people to run faster so at least they remain standing still, not falling behind. A decade ago, for example, most lay persons had no comprehension when someone spoke about biotechnology and gene therapy. Now they are boning up on the subject, usually after first-hand experience with a disease like Alzheimer's in the family.

But if it is not the pace of change and it is not the complexity, what *is* the wellspring for current public alienation toward science, an alienation that is producing this widening chasm of incomprehension? I believe the roots lie in a widespread misconception about what scientists do and how they do it. And a large part of that misconception arises from misleading images which scientists have let persist because it suited their ends.

First among the misleading images comes the heroic myth. That is the idea that science speaks with absolute finality and assuredness, lifts every veil of complexity and confusion and guarantees inevitable outcomes. This myth hoists scientists onto what has been called the "Superman Hook". It sounds almost like a caricature, the most extreme forms of determinism and reductionism. In fact, during what we now call the Science Wars, more than a few scientists publicly took positions not all that far removed from this. And if my reading of *Consilience* is accurate, Edward O. Wilson still does. More importantly, it is what many people expect from knowledge-seekers in general — the expert who will make all clear.

I do not have a public opinion survey to buttress this claim. So let me speak anecdotally, casually and autobiographically, in the best traditions of Charles Percy Snow. In terms of a ring-side seat on the public perception of science and scientists, nothing comes close to being the staff science-writer for the largest newspaper in Canada. From senior editors at the newspaper to anonymous e-mailers, there is a never-ending demand from people who say science should be able to give a straightforward answer to many questions: about survival of the cod fishery, about genetically modified potatoes, about working moms, about gambling, about youth crime and so on. Yet science, indeed any specialized field of knowledge, cannot possibly live up to this myth. It has to deal in complex truths. It cannot, for instance, prove that silicone breast implants are safe, as one of the advocates demanded.

Instinctively, many people realize that science is all too human, that it cannot tell us what ought to be done but only the consequences of what might be done. They know from past experience that science is fallible and incomplete. Yet they have grown up with the heroic myth and at one level they desperately want it to be true. The result is resentment at the clash between what they know to be true and what they want to be true, and a turning toward sources that will provide "black-and-white" answers.

A second source of alienation is the fundamentally flawed concepts of science held by most of the public: science as something concerned with *things* while the arts and humanities are concerned with *ideas*, science as the experimental method, science as the study of the material world. Yet there is a rich literature which says otherwise, starting with Arthur Koestler's *The Act of Creation* and reaching forward to June Goodfield's *An Imagined World*, an account of five years in the scientific growth and maturing of a gifted experimental biologist. These accounts make clear the vital role of imagination in science. I do not mean creativity. No member of the public disputes that creativity is involved in performing science, although most will be thinking of the "eureka moment" rather than the real creativity of importing a paradigm or a technique from one branch of science to solve a problem in another.

But "imagination" has dubious connotations, ones that cause some scientists to scurry for cover as well. They should not. Instead they should talk openly about the very real place for imagination in the best scientific thinking. After all, what is super-string theory anyhow but a very real triumph of creative imagination.

Tackling both these misconceptions, the heroic myth and the "just-the-facts-ma'am" image, will help the public see science as part of society, part of a human and social process and not something separate. The result should be more realistic expectations of the sort of answers that science can provide. The idea that myths bedevil communication between knowledge-seekers and society generally is hardly new. Nor is the observation that scientists and others in the knowledge academies need to explain themselves better. But perhaps, like Snow's two cultures, they are ideas whose time has come.

To illustrate the dangers of the split between the sciences and humanities, Snow used the metaphor of someone trying to grasp the meaning of a vital statement being made in a language where they knew only the occasional word. He was concerned that because the scientific and non-scientific culture could not talk to one another, Western society would be denied the sort of creative change that occurred at the "clashing point".

CONCLUSION

Today, the situation is both better and worse. Despite the frustrations of people like zoologist Martin Wells, the comprehension gaps have been shrinking among the various branches of natural science, as demonstrated by the reach of John Maddox's *What Remains to be Discovered*. I would even argue that the balance has lately improved among the natural sciences, the humanities and the social sciences, which C.P. Snow saw as an emerging third culture. But so wide is the chasm of incomprehension between the knowledge priesthood and the rest of society that my weak flashlight has not been able to so much as flicker on to the other side. If only closing that gap were as simple as learning a new language. But it is not. So enormous is the gap that even with the best intentions it cannot be bridged by the knowledge-seekers acting alone, although their participation is essential. Of course, journalists have a critical role to play as well, starting with noticing that there is a problem. But we need a lot more: leadership from politicians, inspiration from artists, guidance from parents, and instruction from teachers. In order to make a difference all these players must first be able to peer across the chasm.

In his final summing-up, in a collection of essays and speeches entitled *Public Affairs*, Snow (1971) explained that he was publishing the collection because he had nothing more to add. He was, he admitted, increasingly pessimistic that the warning he had tried to sound in 1959 was going to be heeded.

I share that pessimism.

REFERENCES

Adams, D. (1989), *Life, the Universe and Everything*, New York: Harmony Books.

Dreifus, C. (1998), "He Studied Squid and Octopus, Then He Ate Them", *The New York Times*, December 8.

Koestler, A. (1964), *The Act of Creation*, London: Hutchinson.

Maddox, J. (1998), *What Remains to Be Discovered*, New York: Martin Kessler Books.

Sagan, C. (1996), *The Demon-Haunted World: Science as a Candle in the Dark*, New York: Random House.

Snow, C.P. (1961), *Science and Government*, Cambridge, MA: Harvard University Press.

_____ (1965), *The Two Cultures and a Second Look: An expanded version of the two cultures and the scientific revolution*, Cambridge: Cambridge University Press.

_____ (1971), *Public Affairs*, New York: Scribner.

Watson, J.D. (1968), *The Double Helix: A Personal Account of the Discovery of the Structure of DNA*, London: Weidenfeld & Nicolson.

Wilson, E.O. (1998), *Consilience: The Unity of Knowledge*, New York: Knopf.

PART II

BEYOND THE ENDLESS FRONTIER OF SCIENCE

CHAPTER 3

Working with Canada's S&T Policy: Three Years of Learning

T.A. Brzustowski

INTRODUCTION

In this paper, I offer some observations about the Canadian science and technology (S&T) policy from the vantage point of NSERC.[1] In particular, I am interested in the effects of the latest S&T policy in the three years since its publication in 1996. My purpose is to continue the discussion of Canadian S&T policy that was started by John Meisel at the first conference on Statistics, Science and Public Policy held three years ago (Meisel, 1998). A preliminary version of the present paper, prepared well before the 1999 federal budget, was presented at Queen's University a few months ago (Brzustowski, 1998).

John Meisel's (1998) paper was very critical. He did not like much of what he saw of many government efforts to produce an S&T policy in Canada, including the most recent review that led to the latest version. The processes were led by government in all cases, hence, I suppose, the priority given to Caesar in the title.

Nevertheless, the Government of Canada has done many good things in the support of research in the last three years. I refer particularly to making the NCE[2] programme permanent, to the creation of the CFI[3] to help provide a long-needed renewal of research infrastructure, to the restoration of granting council budget cuts in the 1998 budget, and to additional funding in all three areas, as well as a massive new investment in health research, in the recent 1999 budget.[4] Maybe the S&T policy is better than it seemed three years ago.

A BIAS ON POLICY-MAKING

Before starting to discuss policy, I must declare my biases. I do not like the dictionary definitions of policy. I find them too narrow, all talking about a course of action adopted by this or that group to achieve stated goals, presumably their own. I prefer to think of policy, and particularly public policy, in much broader terms. I think of it as a broad framework to guide decisions and actions, of both the custodians of the policy and those affected by it, which are intended to achieve stated goals that are at least broadly understood, if not widely accepted. Underpinning that framework there must be some evidence that the proposed decisions and actions will produce the desired effects. Beyond that, the framework must be based on an understanding of the possibilities of time and place, on a recognition of relevant influences that the policy might bring into play, including explicitly the values, history, culture and condition of those on whom the success of the policy will depend. I would also hope that the basis of any policy would be an accurate perception of the environment in which it is expected to operate, and that the policy could accommodate unexpected changes in that environment.

In my opinion, the weak link in that chain is the understanding of causal linkages.

An additional problem bedevils S&T policy-making, and that is a frequent lack of precision in the use of language. If terms such as "innovation" are not used consistently within the S&T community, one could hardly expect them to be used more consistently by the public policy community, few of whom have any experience in S&T. The problem is that imprecise labels tend to stick, particularly if they are simple and snappy, and that may create ambiguities that confuse the policy process, or worse.

THE 1996 S&T STRATEGY

Let us now consider what the current S&T policy of the Government of Canada (Canada, 1996) actually says. First, it is called a federal S&T strategy and not a policy.[5] Second, it sets three goals:

1.   sustainable job creation and economic growth;
2.   improved quality of life; and
3.   advancement of knowledge;

and four core activities of the government to achieve those goals:

1. funding and performing scientific research to support the mandates of departments and agencies;
2. supporting research in universities and colleges, Networks of Centres of Excellence and other non-governmental research institutions;
3. supporting private sector research and technology development; and
4. providing information and analysis, and building networks.

Much of the rest of the strategy deals more specifically with the research done within government agencies and departments.

I am sure that John Meisel was right when he said that many university researchers were very disappointed that the policy did not list the specific fields of research that are deemed important to Canada, that there was no priority list for major projects, that the issue of the balance between basic and applied research was not addressed, that there was no promise of an increase in research funding, etc. These issues emerged in the public consultation phase of the process, and that raised expectations that they might be addressed in the strategy. The disappointment might have been all the more keen because some other countries conduct elaborate foresight and planning exercises and produce very detailed S&T policies that address such issues in great detail.

But let us move beyond the disappointment, and consider how many of the goals and core activities in the S&T strategy are relevant to the support of university research that is NSERC's mandate. Individual researchers might quickly focus on the third goal (advancement of knowledge) and the second core activity (supporting research in universities and colleges, Networks of Excellence and other non-governmental research institutions). However, the expectation of government is that NSERC will contribute to all three goals. Moreover, the university groups lobbying for increased research support certainly claim that university research is essential for all three goals. This is an important point, and worth a brief digression.

A Digression

I will move to a very different critique of science policy, in a book on U.S. policy entitled *Frontiers of Illusion* by Daniel Sarewitz (1996).

The perspective of Sarewitz is very different from John Meisel's, in that his criticism reflects much more on the scientific community and their beliefs and behaviours than it does on the policy-makers in government.[6] Sarewitz is very critical of the "myths" that form the basis of U.S. science policy, and the first one of these is the myth of the "infinite benefit", the promise expressed by the U.S. research community and accepted by U.S. politicians that more and more research will inevitably meet the first two goals of sustainable job creation and economic growth, and improved quality of life. The basis of the criticism is that this has not happened. There are lots of new gadgets, but people do not have the increased leisure time that had been promised, and the gap between rich and poor, the north and south, is widening rather than closing.

In the present context, it is most interesting that the myth of the infinite benefit has never been embraced in Canada. Indeed, the advocates of increased public funding for research have felt obliged time and again to demonstrate in specific terms how past investments in university research have produced economic benefits or contributed to the high quality of life that Canadians enjoy today. So, even though the support of university research is listed among the four core activities of the government in the S&T policy, I am not sure how widely within government it was associated with the first two goals of job creation and economic growth and improvements in the quality of life.

WORKING WITHIN THE S&T STRATEGY

NSERC is expected to focus on the second of the core activities, but not to the exclusion of the others. Indeed, these activities all receive considerable attention in our research partnership programmes.

One challenge that had to be met just as the new policy appeared (and, as it turned out, for a long time before that) was to make it known within the Government of Canada just what NSERC was and what it did. It was a shock for me to learn how few people in Ottawa knew about NSERC, and how often the knowledge was incomplete, inaccurate, or both.

That need was met with a consistent communication strategy. Its point of departure is a carefully crafted paragraph which, after three years, is now firmly embedded in the NSERC catechism and appears in all our communications.

NSERC is the national instrument for making strategic investments in Canada's intellectual resources in science and technology. NSERC invests in three aspects of university research in the natural sciences and engineering: basic research supported by grants, project research supported through university-industry partnerships, and advanced education of research students in both kinds of research.

But to get to that language we had to deal with the issue of basic versus applied research. For many years there had been a debate on university campuses that might best be called "a clash of concerns" exacerbated by constraints in funding. I do not think I am drawing an exaggerated caricature when I describe it in the following terms. Those doing basic research were concerned that they would be denied funding because their work did not have immediate commercial application.[7] Moreover, one also heard that applied work was intellectually inferior, and should not be funded on grounds of quality. On the other side, those doing applied research were concerned that they would be denied funding because their work did not lead to enough refereed papers in the archive journals. And, in any case, too much money was being wasted on useless pure research that nobody needed. The debate was subdued most of the time, with only occasional public eruptions, but it had the potential to be very destructive in the long term.

The language of the debate was telling. On the one side there was research that was "basic, fundamental, pure, curiosity-driven, investigator-driven", uplifting words all. On the other side the language was "applied, industrial, targeted", good solid words that held out the promise of utility.[8]

By contrast, biomedical researchers seemed very fortunate because they did not feel the need to engage in that debate. Even researchers studying the most fundamental processes in the cell always seemed to have a clear idea of how their results might be used to improve health. It now appears that this good fortune of biomedical researchers is not the exception to a bad rule, but rather the basis of a good one. In a recent book called *Pasteur's Quadrant*, Donald Stokes (1997) points out that the one-dimensional view of research as basic or applied is grossly inadequate. He demonstrates in convincing fashion that the purpose of research should be characterized by two dimensions: new understanding and new use. Pasteur's quadrant refers to research done to find both a new understanding and a new use. Bohr's quadrant locates research conducted only to find a new understanding, and Edison's locates research intended only to find a new use.[9]

Stokes mentions something else in *Pasteur's Quadrant* that I find important and disturbing. He claims that the very term "basic research" was coined by Vannevar Bush, and that the dichotomy between basic and applied research was created by him in order to maintain control of U.S. federal funding of research in the hands of the research community at the end of the World War II.[10] If this is true, then it provides an example of something referred to earlier, wrong labels that stick for a long time and create problems.

Be that as it may, in 1996 the balance between basic and applied research was an issue NSERC had to deal with rather urgently. Conceptually it was easy. Once we moved beyond the labels and examined what people were doing when they did one or the other kind of research, it became very clear that there were no opposites here, no poles of a dichotomy. For that reason, NSERC chose to label the two kinds of research that we sponsor "basic research" and "project research" — two different activities, but clearly not opposites. Moreover, we could not trust that people would always interpret these two phrases in the same way, so we defined them through a list of attributes. Three years later, the debate now seems to be muted. It is now generally recognized that many excellent researchers are very successful in basic research and project research at the same time, and have been for years. On reflection, what else could one have expected?

It now seems that one more element is needed to complete these definitions of two kinds of research, namely the definition of research itself. I find the dictionary definitions of research inadequate in that they describe the form of the activity but do not suggest its goal. And the two scientific encyclopedias in my office do not define it at all.[11]

For that reason, I offer the following very general definition: "Research is the process of learning what is not yet known." I think that this definition of research embraces both of Stokes' categories: research done to gain a new understanding and research done to find a new use. The definitions of basic and project research are listed in Tables 1 and 2.

This definition of project research corresponds closely to what John Ziman (1998) and others call "post-academic science" and what Michael Gibbons (1998) calls "Mode 2 research". The preceding definition of basic research corresponds to what these authors call "academic science" and "Mode 1 research", respectively.

There was also a policy issue lurking behind the debate about basic and project research, the allocation of resources between programmes. The research community was greatly concerned that funding of basic research was being reduced to provide more money for project research in partnership with industry. This was another issue that many academic participants in the S&T strategy review had expected to see addressed in the new policy. It was not. But the NSERC Council had decided in 1995 that it would maintain the level of spending for grants that support basic research, even as NSERC's total budget was declining. That decision clearly indicated that the Council believed in the importance of basic research, but since the S&T policy is silent on that point there are still some university researchers in Canada who continue to worry about it.

Table 1: NSERC Definition of Basic Research

Basic Research in the universities has these attributes:

Its *object* is discovery.

Its *context* is the state of knowledge in the field worldwide.

Its *format* is a programme of research activity defined by the investigators.

Its *merit* lies in the importance and excellence of the programme, as judged by peers.

It *educates* highly qualified people in finding the sources of current knowledge, in creating new knowledge in the context of current advances around the world, and in understanding its trends and its limitations.

Its *results* are exposed to the review of peers and published openly without additional delay.

Priority of discovery is generally the issue, more than the ownership of intellectual property.

It may lead to profound *benefits to humanity* in the long term, but they cannot be predicted in the short term.

If it has any *short-term economic benefits*, they are incidental, and their presence or absence should not skew either the funding decisions or the policies of research support.

Table 2: NSERC Definition of Project Research

Project Research in the universities has these attributes:

Its *object* is to solve a problem or achieve some desired result that can be specified to a significant extent but cannot be produced with existing knowledge.

Its *context* is defined much more by an area of industrial activity than by a discipline, and the project may involve research in more than one discipline.

Its *format* is a project whose design, schedule, milestones, budget, deliverables, etc. are defined by the investigators and their partners.

Its *merit* is judged in terms of the quality of both the research proposed and the design of the project.

It *educates* highly qualified people in finding the sources of current knowledge and in creating new knowledge, and it *trains* them in putting it to productive use.

Its *results* may have direct economic value, and therefore it requires clarity about the ownership of intellectual property.

The open publication of research *results* may be delayed by the need to protect intellectual property, but any portion of the research work being done by graduate students must, nevertheless, meet the university's academic requirements for a degree.

It has *short-term economic benefits* that are sufficiently predictable and desirable to attract partners from industry and other sectors to invest their own resources in it, and it may have *long-term economic and other benefits to humanity* as well.

The *training* it provides is an immediate benefit for the industrial partner — the graduate students and research staff working on it become available for employment by the partner at the end of the project, and are ready to be productive in related work.

Three years later, it is clear that the Council's decision supports all three goals of the S&T strategy. Basic research is associated with the advancement of knowledge, and we could always trace big improvements in our quality of life to the discoveries of researchers whose goal had been to advance knowledge. But it is also known that basic research is the source of many brand new start-up companies that create high-quality jobs and valuable exports. And we have learned that established industries now look to basic research in the universities as the source of ideas for their own radical innovations.

All that to say that a decision by the NSERC Council, some clarity in language and consistency as well as persistence in communications resolved some difficult issues that had many policy implications. The S&T policy rightly leaves such questions to departments and agencies.

Here is another example. NSERC takes very seriously the government's goals for obtaining an economic benefit for Canada in return for the investment of public funds. Our Partnership Research programmes were designed to connect researchers who generate new knowledge with those in the economy and society at large who might use the new knowledge productively. But such connections can raise difficult policy issues dealing with the ownership of intellectual property (IP). The national S&T policy is silent on IP issues, but it is clear that if we are to work toward government goals then the IP issues must be solved along the way. That is being done, not at NSERC Council, not even at the programme level, but between the universities and their partners. NSERC offers help when help is needed, but its driving interest is only that the partners reach some agreement on how they will deal with IP.

The 1998 budget provides yet another example of the freedom that the granting councils enjoy under the present S&T policy. All of our budget cuts were rolled back, and funding was restored to the 1994-95 levels. For NSERC that meant $71 million dollars more than we had planned for in 1998-99. The instruction accompanying this large increase (17 per cent) was the following:

These new research and development resources will focus on two key areas: (i) increased support to graduate students engaged in research through scholarships, post-doctoral fellowships and project grants; and (ii) enhanced partnerships between universities and industry (Canada. Department of Finance, 1998, p. 78).

This instruction left it up to NSERC to decide how the money was to be allocated. Thus, the Council decided in June 1998 on the balance between the number of new scholarships and fellowships and the increase in their value, on how much money to add to research grants to provide for more support of assistants-in-research, on how much to invest in the Research Partnership programme, etc. In the event, we were able to start addressing the most pressing problems that researchers had brought to NSERC's attention. The S&T policy did not explicitly help in the process, but it is clear that both the Minister of Finance and NSERC knew they were working within the same framework.

But now an issue is looming which might penetrate through the framework of the S&T strategy. It has to do with the direct and indirect costs of research. For the twenty years of NSERC's life, and before that at the National Research Council of Canada (NRC),[12] the federal grants have been paying only the direct costs of the research. The indirect costs were absorbed by the universities, which get their funding from the provinces. This process of taking funds that come through two constitutionally distinct routes and bringing them together in the lab where research is done has worked well. The two funding streams tracked pretty much in parallel, and the proportions stayed roughly constant. However, a problem is now starting to emerge. The two funding streams are diverging. The universities' ability to pay for the indirect costs is declining, just as the federal grants that cover the direct costs are starting to rise. If these funding streams diverge enough, an adjustment will become necessary. And that would be a federal-provincial issue that could drag research funding into the realm of Canadian constitutional negotiations. I think that everything should be done to avoid that because of the uncertainties and disruptions that might result.

Let me end on a lighter note. To work within the S&T strategy one also needs to understand the political realities of government. Without wishing to trivialize the issues in any way, I want to illustrate some of what I mean by two observations that might be called the First and Second Laws of Research Funding. As in thermodynamics, the second law is much more subtle than the first.

First Law of Research Funding: There is less and less of more of the same.

Governments have the political need to announce new measures that deal with important problems in modern ways. The public gives little credit for correcting mistakes, and reversals of direction, however justified, are too easily dismissed as flip-flops. If more of the same is what is really needed, then an extraordinarily strong case must be made for it. The restoration of the budget cuts of the granting councils was a measure that did this. It was a very strong political statement, which would not have been made if the government were not convinced that the S&T policy was working well.

Second Law of Research Funding: If new money becomes available for project A and enough loud voices in the research community claim that project B would be much better, then the most likely outcome is that the money for A will be lost, and that no money will be found for B.

The availability of new money, that is, outside the established competitive programme structure, for some particular research project does not necessarily mean that this money was ever available for research in general. It may simply be the case that the research project in question meets some specific needs of the government, as well as the scientific criteria of quality. Criticizing such a project on scientific grounds may eventually persuade the government that the quality is inadequate, and that funding should not be provided, but it is hardly likely to redirect the funds to some different project. Simply put, it is important for the research community to know when to compete and when to support one another.

CONCLUSIONS

What, finally, is my assessment of Canada's S&T policy after living with it for three years? On balance, it is very positive, and here are some reasons for that.

First, the policy works for university research in the natural sciences and engineering. It has obviously made it possible for government to do good things to help NSERC help the natural sciences and engineering research community, and it has allowed us to work with the researchers to solve important problems. I am well aware, of course, that success cannot be attributed to policy alone. It depends also on trust, on communications and on mutual understanding. I believe that a climate of trust is developing between the research community and NSERC, and between NSERC and the government. Such trust requires that each entity understand the needs and problems of the others, that it have realistic expectations of what each can contribute to the total effort, and that it be prepared to give credit when credit is due.

Success also requires clear and consistent communications in all directions, not just among NSERC, the research community and government, but also with the public. The government must be assured that the public will support its spending on university research, and the research community itself must be active in obtaining that support. After all, the research community is competing for scarce public funds with many other intelligent and dedicated Canadians who are just as devoted to their causes, just as convinced of the importance of those causes to the nation, and traditionally much more skilled and active politically.

But the above statements might be made in the context of almost any S&T policy. So what are the particularly favourable features of the current one?

If beauty is in the eye of the beholder, then flaws may be in the eye of the critic. Canada's S&T policy is not the detailed, prescriptive and exhaustive Cartesian course of action that many had expected, and it is certainly not the outcome of a progression of tidy processes neatly building on one another. On the contrary, the latest result of our lurching progress to define an S&T policy is a broad framework that leaves agencies and departments with a lot of room for diversity in initiatives that might contribute to achieving sustainable job creation and economic growth, improved quality of life and advancement of knowledge. That freedom comes at a price; it is more work to develop initiatives and write your own policies than to implement a detailed prescriptive policy from the centre. But the great benefit is that the details of policy are developed by those familiar with the current state of the research community on whom its success depends.

In hindsight, the form of the policy was very fortunate in another way. The current Canadian S&T policy was formulated at a time when the Government of Canada was reducing its spending in all areas in order to eliminate an unsustainable deficit. The 1995 budget prescribed severe cuts even in the support of university research. It would have been an unfortunate legacy of those tough times if the S&T policy had taken the form of a rigid set of prescriptions that reflected the fiscal circumstances of the day. As it is, the deficit is gone and the broad S&T policy framework has enabled the government to restore the cuts and raise the support for university research to a level that is an historical high, if still short of what is needed.

The general form of Canada's S&T policy is appropriate in one more important way: it accommodates learning. I believe that the government now knows that Canada is much more dependent on university research than are the countries we trade with for the necessary transformation to a value-added economy in all sectors. I believe also that industry and government now understand the strategic value of basic research both as an instrument for honing the nation's competence and as a source of ideas for radical innovations. I believe, as well, that the research community has learned much about networking and working with industrial partners, and has come to appreciate that as researchers and as educators of the next generation they are uniquely qualified to deliver a strategic return on the resources the public has invested in them. And I believe that all three groups have learned about the importance of innovation, and the role that they each must play in our innovation system.

All that learning has taken place within the broad framework of the S&T policy. It has not been constrained by rigid prescriptions of relationships and interactions that would have reflected an earlier, and less adequate, state of understanding of Canada's innovation system.

Many of today's problems that involve S&T still need to be solved, and we can only guess at the challenges of tomorrow. However, I believe that Canada will be well served by the current S&T policy for some time to come.

NOTES

1. The Natural Sciences and Engineering Research Council of Canada, the federal agency that supports research in science and engineering in Canadian universities.

2. Networks of Centres of Excellence, a programme that had been scheduled to sunset in 1998 was made permanent in the February 1997 budget. The NCE programme is administered by the granting councils and Industry Canada.

3. Canada's Foundation for Innovation was created in the February 1997 budget with an endowment of $800 million to provide universities and research hospitals with new research infrastructure funded on a matching basis (40 per cent federal, 60 per cent other sources) with the institutions and their partners.

4. "The Budget Plan 1999" (Canada, 1999), announced among other things a $25 million increase in NSERC's annual budget, an additional endowment of $200 million for the CFI, an increase of $30 million (63 per cent) in the annual budget of the NCE programme, and new investments in university health research adding up to $390 million over the next three fiscal years; see pp. 110-115, 93-101.

5. Perhaps inaccurately. This is not a plan of action with objectives, specific action plans, milestones, indicators and provisions for updating. There are accompanying action plans from departments, etc., but the central document seems much more of a policy than a strategy.

6. Perhaps this means that U.S. researchers have more influence on their nation's S&T policy than Canadian researchers have on theirs. If so, it might be worth finding out how and why.

7. "Scientists would be penalized for making the wrong discovery" — John Polanyi, in a speech, 1996.

8. This reminds me of the saying of my colleague Charles Pascal, former Deputy Minister of Education and Training in Ontario, who would call this kind of debate "A hardening of the categories".

9. Stokes does not name the quadrant where neither new understanding nor new use is a motive for the research. It is difficult to think of examples of work that would fall in that quadrant and still be called research.

10. Vannevar Bush, *Science: The Endless Frontier*, report submitted in 1945 to President Harry S Truman of the United States, and widely considered to be the basis for science policy in the United States in the second half of the twentieth century.

11. Van Nostrand's *Scientific Encyclopedia*, Fourth Edition, 1968 has no index and no entry for research in the text; the McGraw-Hill *Concise Encyclopedia of Science and Technology*, Third Edition, 1994 has no entry for research either in the text or in the index.

12. Until the creation of NSERC in 1978, university research was supported through the Office of Grants and Scholarships of National Research Council of Canada (NRC).

REFERENCES

Brzustowski, T. (1998), "Living with Canada's S&T Policy — The Savants and Caesar", paper presented at the launch of the Bader Chair in Organic Chemistry, Queen's University, November 2.

Canada (1996), *Science and Technology for the New Century: Summary*, Cat. No. C2-290/1996-1, Ottawa: Supply and Services Canada.

Canada. Department of Finance (1998), *The Budget Plan 1998*, Cat. No. F1-23/1998-1E, Ottawa: Supply and Services Canada.

_____ (1999), *The Budget Plan 1999*, Cat. No. F1-23/1999-3E. Ottawa: Supply and Services Canada.

Gibbons, M. (1998), "Higher Education Relevance in the 21st Century", paper presented at the UNESCO World Conference on Higher Education, Paris, October 5-9

Meisel, J. (1998), "Caesar and the Savants: Some Socio-Political Contexts of Science and Technology in Canada", in *Statistics, Science and Public Policy*, ed. A.M. Herzberg and I. Krupka, Kingston: Queen's University, pp. 153-177.

Sarewitz, D. (1996), *Frontiers of Illusion — Science, Technology and the Politics of Progress*, Philadelphia: Temple University Press.

Stokes, D.E. (1997), *Pasteur's Quadrant — Basic Science and Technological Innovation*, Washington, D.C.: The Brookings Institution.

Ziman, J. (1998), "Why Must Scientists Become More Ethically Sensitive than They Used To Be?" *Science* 282:1813-1814.

CHAPTER 4

"Unlocking Our Future": A New U.S. Science Policy?

R.E. Taylor

Unlocking Our Future is the title of a September 1998 report to the U.S. Congress from the House of Representatives' Committee on Science. The study was initiated by the Republican leadership of the House to develop "a new, sensible, coherent, long-range Science and Technology Policy".[1] The study was to go beyond the "Endless Frontier".

Representative Vernon Ehlers (at the time, the only Ph.D. in the House and Vice-Chairman of the House Science and Technology Committee) was chosen to direct the study. The result was *Unlocking Our Future*, subtitled *Toward a New National Science Policy*. In the overview, the report is characterized as "not a major overhaul, but rather a fine tuning and rejuvenation" of the existing science policy, so it will not go much beyond the present frontier. Two things have happened in recent years that might be expected to cause significant changes in federal research policy: the growing pressure on the federal budget from the entitlement programs, and the end of the "Cold War", which has led to the feeling that new national security research is now less important.

The Ehlers' report is rather long with three full pages of a "Summary of Recommendations". There are about thirty of them and some are quite sweeping, such as

- "To maintain our nation's economic strength and international competitiveness, Congress should make stable and substantial

funding for fundamental scientific research a high priority"
(p. 39).

- "Priority for federal funding should be placed on *fundamental research*" (p. 39, emphasis added).

Others are quite detailed:

- "Scientists and engineers should be required to divulge their credentials, provide a resume, and indicate their funding sources and affiliations when formally offering expert advice to decision-makers" (p. 41).
- "Universities should consider offering scientists, as part of their graduate training, the opportunity to take at least one course in journalism or communication. Journalism schools should also encourage journalists to take at least one course in scientific *writing*" (p. 43, emphasis added).

The most important recommendations dealing with federal support are:

1. Stable and substantial funding for fundamental scientific research (for economic reasons).
2. Priority on fundamental research (indicates Republican's aversion to funding of industrial research — do not interfere with the free market, the private sector should take responsibility for the performance of research).
3. A broad spectrum of scientific disciplines, mathematics and engineering should be supported.
4. Stick to missions for research funded at or through federal agencies, laboratories, etc.
5. The report emphasizes education and suggests changes to the current emphasis. The federal government has very limited responsibilities for education compared with state and local jurisdictions.

In my view, these are the recommendations that might have a noticeable impact on the support of science in the United States if they were to be translated into action. Even then U.S. science policy would be very similar to the status quo.

If one compares the Ehlers report and Bush proposal (see Table 1), there are a couple of interesting differences in outlook. The reasons given for government support seem to have narrowed (though Ehlers

Table 1: Comparison of U.S. Scientific Policy Reports in 1945
and 1998

	Endless Frontier *(V. Bush)* *1945*	*Unlocking Our Future* *(V. Ehler)* *1998*
WHY?	Health Public welfare (i.e., the Economy) Defence	Economic benefits
HOW?	A national research foundation	~ Status quo NSF, DOE, NASA, NIH Military services
WHAT?	Basic research Applied research (including military)	Basic research (military?)
WHICH?	Hard sciences Mathematics Engineering Biology, medical Education	Hard sciences Mathematics Engineering Life sciences Social sciences Education
WHERE?	Universities National laboratories Industry	Universities National laboratories
HOW MUCH?	~ M$ 33 ($1946)	~ 10^{10} ($1998)

does mention that research is important for defence, and medical research may be missing in his report because legislative responsibility for health matters does not rest with the House Science Committee).

The present mechanisms for science funding by the federal government are actually far removed from the strategy outlined in the Bush report. Bush wanted to establish an independent, civilian-controlled agency that would oversee *all* government-supported research and make grants to universities for research. That idea was never adopted and even a much weaker version, which kept more control in the Executive Branch, was vetoed by President Truman in 1947. In 1950, a National Science Foundation (NSF) was created, but by that time both the Atomic Energy Commission and the Office of Naval Research were acting as major funding agencies for university research, so the role of the NSF was much more limited than imagined by Bush. The Ehlers report does not question the existing channels of support, which come from many parts of the federal government.

Bush wanted his foundation to control even military research. Ehlers is not clear about the military, but does believe that market forces should determine the level of *applied* research without government interference.

There is general agreement about which sciences should be supported, although the social sciences were added to the NSF portfolio some time ago. The Republican Party feels strongly that government should not support applied research in industry, in contrast to Bush's view.

The most spectacular change in the fifty years between the reports is the difference in how much support the government should provide. Bush thought that thirty-three million dollars (1946 dollars) would be about right for the first year's budget and estimated that four or five times that amount would be needed a decade later. Even allowing for inflation, the government's support of science has reached levels that would have seemed impossible in 1946. In the U.S. federal budget for next year, science (including the National Aeronautics and Space Administration, NASA) gets about twenty billion dollars. This is a large number, but still a small percentage of government discretionary spending. Arguments that the United States can no longer afford to finance large scientific projects reflect choices in spending patterns, rather than true "affordability".

What justifies the expenditures on research by the federal government?

Science will make you rich. This argument is ancient and it is now the major justification for governmental support. Even before the Christian era, the alchemists began a search for methods of transforming base metals into gold. I do not know how their research was financed, but surely those ancient alchemists must have sometimes traded on the greed of others. The search, 2,000 years of searching, demonstrates the futility of applied research without some basic knowledge, and also demonstrates that even unsuccessful applied research may lead to fundamental advances in knowledge. The alchemists isolated many of the chemical elements. The alchemists had given up their ancient goals before the United States came into existence. Governmental support of science was still a long way off in 1776.

The U.S. Constitution mentions science just once, in Section 8 (Taxes, Fiscal Policy). Clause 8, "[Congress shall have the power] to promote the Progress of Science and useful Arts, by securing for limited times to Authors and Inventors the exclusive right to their respective writings and Discoveries." There is no indication that the new republic felt any responsibility to support scientific research.

The Patent Office was established in 1790 and interestingly enough, the Land Grant Universities (1863) resulted in both basic and applied research in agriculture with costs shared between federal and state governments. Over the years the federal government also established several scientific service bureaus: the Coast Survey, Weights and Measures, Census, Weather, etc. Apart from this, federal support for basic research was uncommon and this was accepted by the scientists of those days.

Science: The Endless Frontier was the first time a strong argument for governmental support of basic research was made on the basis that increased scientific capital would bring "prosperity and full employment". Bush also argued for vigorous applied research in government and industry. Here he was quite conservative about the federal role, pointing out the need for the government's aid in the development of scientific talent, along with better pay and working conditions for government employees in applied research. He also made some modern sounding noises about tax incentives and technology transfer for industry.

The Ehlers report makes the argument that science is essential to economic strength and the overall health of the nation, and this is the report's principal justification for government support.

Science will keep you healthy. The alchemists were there first, about 1300 AD, expanding their field of interest beyond economics and adding a search for immortality. Again this applied research was not successful, and even led to conflict with the church. (The church has a vested interest in mortality.) Basic medical research was not a government priority in the Middle Ages, but there was progress all the same and lots of public health improvements later on in the 1800s. Bush began his report with a forthright call for "Scientific progress in the war against disease", pointing out that, although great progress in medicine had been made between the wars, it was time for federal support of medical research. Bush's logic was accepted and medical science has added many years to our lives, though we have not yet reached the alchemists' goal. The war on cancer was not entirely successful, not enough knowledge for such a huge applied science effort, but like the alchemists, there was a great deal of useful basic fallout. The Ehlers report ignores this area of research, probably because the legislative responsibility for health matters does not rest with the House Science Committee.

Science will make you stronger than your enemy. War has been a major factor in U.S. science policy. Major changes in science policy have usually occurred during (or just following) wartime. During the Civil War, technology became important: iron ships, steam engine, armaments. The National Academy of Sciences (NAS) was founded in 1863 to bring scientific advice to bear on government activities. The charter specifically forbids paying scientists, effectively limiting the power of the organization in the years before World War I.

The advice of scientists was again needed (and actively sought) during World War I. The technological questions had become quite complex by this time and a National Research Council (NRC) was formed in the United States. After the war, NRC continued as a branch of the NAS, which allowed the government to pay for science advice, much of it "applied". During the Depression, the government took an increased role in society and there was backhanded support of basic research in some projects of the Work Projects Administration along with isolated support for a few big schemes, but there was still not much enthusiasm in Congress or the Executive Branch for general support of basic science.

Technology assumed a dominant role in warfare during World War II: radar, rockets, A-bombs, design improvements to conventional weapons, and so on. The A-bomb in particular demonstrated the potential importance of both fundamental and applied research — without the work on sub-atomic physics in the half-century before the war, no one would have suspected that such a weapon could be built and without the truly incredible applied research effort (the most impressive international science project to date, I would say), the bomb would not have been ready in time to end the war. Science and scientists were becoming more powerful.

Vannevar Bush was deeply involved in the war effort; he headed the Office of Civilian Defense Research and made valuable technical contributions in more than one area. Bush could not have foreseen how important military research and development would become in the thirty-five years following his report.

The support of research tilted strongly toward military research and issues of national security after the USSR tested A-bombs and then H-bombs. Sputnik had a much broader effect: convincing lawmakers that the United States should try for superiority in all scientific fields. There followed a "golden decade" for science support. NASA was established and the United States went to the moon. (The exploits in space were the purest form of "my science is better than your science".)

The war in Vietnam was a factor in the changes that came in the late 1960s and early 1970s. Many universities rejected classified research after the students protested any involvement in the war. Because of this, university research took a beating (i.e., no growth) for several years. Health research was not as controversial and so as the war in Vietnam wound down, the war on cancer began. This is another example of the futility of trying to do applied research before its time and also an example of the benefits to basic science from the by-products of unsuccessful applied research. The weapons race intensified in this period causing increases in the U.S. military research program.

Was Bush right, has science made us rich? It seems clear to most people that basic research has been an important factor in the innovations that generate new products. Estimates of the "high technology" contribution to the U.S. economy run as high as 50 per cent. The role that basic research plays in the high-tech market is not easy to estimate, and there are still some who feel that government support should be reduced, and that progress will occur as a result of "market forces".

Sometimes Vannevar Bush has been accused of using a "linear" model for science-based contributions to the economy.

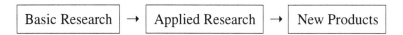

This model is so simple it would make an economist blush and it is easy to find counter examples. Bush certainly knew that applied research has sometimes led to basic discoveries and that new products often open up new possibilities for fundamental research. The Ehlers report insists that he was aware of the various feedback loops and also the possibility that new inventions can sometimes come from fundamental research.

The ending of the Cold War has had significant effects on the federal support of U.S. science. The driving force has shifted toward the economic benefits of research and "accountability" has become the watchword. The Superconducting Super Collider was cancelled, all NASA projects (except the space station) have been scaled back, and so on.

What of the future? I believe that Bush's eloquent arguments for the support of science will continue to prevail, although spending levels may change without much reference to scientific reasoning. There are, of course, legislators who are trying to advance the public good and who believe strongly in one or more of the answers to the "why" question. They are still willing to spend big money on science. Others still harbour some doubts about "useless" research for fuzzy-haired professors with no clear commercial goals in sight. (They believe that the increase in gross domestic product/capita is independent of the amount spent on scientific research and development.) My guess is that funding for science in the United States will grow at about the inflation rate for the country, somewhat less than the inflation rate for research. Within the total research envelope, there is a shift toward biological/medical research and education and that trend will probably continue. The *vision statement* in the Ehlers report reads:

> The United States of America must maintain and improve its pre-eminent position in science and technology in order to advance human understanding of the universe and all it contains, and to improve the lives, health, and freedom of all peoples (1998, p. 4).

We will see if that ambitious vision can be realized without a considerable increase in the existing levels of support.

NOTE

1. Speaker Gingrich's letter states that the United States is operating under a model developed by Vannevar Bush in 1945 in *Science, the Endless Frontier*, which Gingrich says is "no longer valid".

REFERENCES

Bush, V. (1945), *Science: The Endless Frontier*, Report to the President, Washington, D.C.: United States Government Printing Office.

Ehlers, V. (1998), *Unlocking Our Future: Toward a New National Science Policy*, Report to Congress by the House Committee on Science, Washington, D.C.: Government Printing Office.

PART III

SCIENCE AND THE PUBLIC PURSE

CHAPTER 5

Independence, Dependence, Interdependence

P.O. Larsen

INTRODUCTION

Tycho Brahe was a Danish astronomer who lived from 1546 to 1601. He spent his active life on the small island of Hven, about twenty kilometres north of Copenhagen. Here, Tycho Brahe created what today is called an international centre of excellence. He received generous funding for his costly endeavours from the Danish king and the state. In fact, for many years he was given between 1 and 2 per cent of the total income of the Crown. This public support for one individual scientist was at a level never before seen in the uneasy relationship between science and government.

But there were strings attached: Tycho Brahe had many official duties, such as maintaining the light on Kullen in order to guide ships through the Sound to the Baltic. Another job was to look after a chapel at the Cathedral of Roskilde, the chapel where one of the King's forefathers was buried. Tycho Brahe did not carry out his responsibilities. The rain fell through the roof of the chapel and the light on Kullen flickered. In 1597, he fell out with the King and left in search of a new patron. He died in Prague in 1601. This represents the lesson that *scientists are supposed to deliver services in return for public support.*

Tycho Brahe was also expected to help with the calendar, produce medicines and provide horoscopes for the royal family, even though his relationship to astrology is not clear; especially in his last years, he was rather sceptical (Thoren, 1990, pp. 213-219). Lesson number two is that *scientists might have to compromise their freedom of research.*

Tycho Brahe lived in a Lutheran country with the Church and State having common interests. It might not have been problematic for him to question the old system that placed the earth at the centre of the universe, but the subsequent stories of Giordano Bruno and Galileo teach us the third lesson: *some research is unacceptable to society.* He studied Copernicus and ended up by rejecting the heliocentric system. In fact, he compromised: the earth in the middle of the universe, the planets moving around the sun, but the sun and the moon moving around the earth. He believed in circles, in circular motion. It was up to his pupil and successor, Johannes Kepler, to establish the concept of elliptical orbits.

More could be said about Tycho Brahe but it is just relevant to mention that he was the first scientist to be seriously interested in the question of observational error. The lessons from Tycho Brahe, however, are an introduction to my main theme: the interface and interplay between science and the public — the questions of freedom of research and academic freedom, the services that science provides to the public, and the benefits that the "public" wants.

FREEDOM OF RESEARCH AND ACADEMIC FREEDOM

Freedom of research is not a well-defined and absolute concept, nor is it a white and black issue, but it is much more complex. This is just a simple analysis. The first principle is the freedom (or obligation) to draw conclusions based on observations, experiments and methods. This principle must be upheld. Science and research are irretrievably damaged if results can be ordered from the outside or if the scientist bends his results in order to get what he wants. So the first principle is as close to an absolute as is possible in this world.

The second principle is the freedom to publish results and conclusions. Here, however, there are already restrictions, such as financial. Printers' bills must be paid and access to journals is not automatic; editors and referees make all the decisions. There are restrictions on research in private companies, government research institutions and in universities undertaking research on contract. In addition, individual scientists must have their colleagues' acceptance first and cannot rush into print without the agreement of all participants in joint research.

The third principle is the freedom to choose problems and methods. There are obvious, major restrictions here. Resources are scarce and very little research and certainly no experimental research can be done without financial support. Thus, freedom of research cannot be invoked as a final argument against all outside interference.

Academic freedom is not precisely the same as freedom of research, but is based on the tradition of universities. A clear expression of academic freedom is found in the European *Magna Carta* for universities, adopted in 1988 at the Jubilee to celebrate 900 years of the University of Bologna. The *Magna Carta* is in Latin, of course, but these quotations are from the official English version. The paragraphs relevant to the discussion of academic freedom are:

1.   The university is an autonomous institution at the heart of societies differently organized because of geography and historical heritage; it produces, examines, appraises and hands down culture through research and teaching.
2.   To meet the needs of the world around it, its research and teaching must be morally and intellectually independent of all political authority and economic power.
3.   Freedom in research and training is the fundamental principle of university life, and governments and universities, each as far as in them lies, must ensure respect for this fundamental requirement.

Academic freedom is a "mixed bag". Depending on one's point of view, the concept may be characterized as a main part of the official ideology of universities, an historical heritage, an instrument for the protection of rights and privileges, or a necessary independence from governments and other authorities. It is seen as a way to further quality and efficiency in education and research, and an important ingredient in the "social contract" between science and society.

Whatever we choose it is obvious that academic freedom is not absolute. Some might even call it fictitious. Thus, it was stated in the Robbins report in 1963 that there was no freedom for universities without budgetary freedom (Robbins, 1963, p. 230). At least in continental Europe, and Danish universities are part of the continental tradition, budget freedom has not existed for more than one hundred years. There has been tight control of finances. Budgetary freedom has also been curtailed in the United Kingdom in the last decade.

WHAT IS THE PUBLIC ASKING IN RETURN?

Governments, parliaments and taxpayers want value for money. They want quality and efficiency. They also want results — useful results. They want a research system and universities to be open to the surrounding society, sharing knowledge and meeting demands from that society.

This sounds fair enough. The problems arise, however, when the public takes measures to ensure that the demands are met. What sort of measures? And how can they avoid coming into conflict with the essential ingredients of freedom of research and academic freedom? Why is the interface between science and the public important today? It has probably always been on the agenda, but there are a number of good reasons why it has become an important issue today:

1.   The expansion of the research system, including universities, and concomitantly the vast amounts of money involved.
2.   Universities today "take care" of a large fraction of young people. This is the universities' largest cost. The time and potential of the students are assets that must not be wasted. Today, society needs to be careful about its treatment of this resource.
3.   The close relationship between science, technology and economic growth and prosperity. The results of science are useful and necessary.
4.   The pace of change. Adaptability is imperative, especially for science.

The interface between science and society is real, and society has a legitimate interest in what is going on.

WHY NOT LEAVE IT TO THE SCIENTISTS AND TO MARKET FORCES?

Science is a success story, at least it is experienced as a success story by most scientists, as well as by most of the public. Obviously, it is a success in terms of growth, employment and resources. Science has always been able to take care of itself. Research is progressive, and the research system by itself makes room for changes, even revolutions. Science has an inherent capacity for self-regulation. This is because it is about a quest for knowledge, it involves scientists' ambitions and it takes part in the competition in the research system. International competition (and cooperation) is imperative to keep the system moving.

On the other hand all systems, all institutions and nearly all universities are conservative. There are always vested interests to protect. It is so easy to continue research projects by asking for more of the same. The history of science tells us that change has not always been easy. With the wisdom of hindsight it is possible to see that adaptability has been restricted, and that many changes have been implemented by outside pressures. This, at least, is visible in the Danish research system. Is it only valid for Denmark?

Here are a few examples from my experiences at the Danish National Research Foundation. We invested resources in bioinformatics: because we had a few very good scientists here; because biology is going to change in the next decade; because of the vast amounts of information accrued (from the big sequencing projects including the human genome project); and because of new possibilities for handling and exploiting information. But Danish universities have been very reluctant to put bioinformatics on the curriculum. At least, they have not been willing to transfer existing resources or to stop or restrict extrapolation in traditional areas of biology.

We have put resources into research into parasitology because of its importance for human health and for animal husbandry and because of a growing interest in parasitism in connection with fundamental questions in biology, especially evolution. Again Danish universities have not been overly responsive.

There are other reasons besides conservatism for not leaving science to manage itself. Some scientists are guilty of overselling, of promising politicians and the public that they can solve any problem, including problems of a political nature where no amount of research will provide solutions. This is detrimental to the public trust in science.

Then there are those scientists who become greedy. I quote from Cornford's classic *Microcosmographia Academica*. One of the five political parties in academia identified by Cornford is the Adullamites. In his own words: "The Adullamites are dangerous, because they know what they want; and that is, all the money there is going" (Cornford, 1908, pp. 4-5).

Finally, there are some naïve scientists propagating the basic misconception that all scientific research is unpredictable, that unexpected and important results can occur everywhere, and therefore, there should be no planning and no quality control in science. This does not further the trust in science among politicians and bureaucrats.

CAN POLITICIANS AND ADMINISTRATORS MANAGE SCIENCE?

Are politicians that farsighted? My experience is that most politicians want success and publicity, here and now. There was once a Danish politician who was deeply interested in science. He was in charge of the Treasury for seven years, Prime Minister for two years, and had a positive impact on our research system. But he is the only Danish politician in my experience who had the knowledge or wisdom necessary to deal with science and, at the same time, had influence.

What does the public need? And does it *know* what it really needs? Is there a public understanding of the difference between basic and applied research? Or is there a general belief that all science should provide usable results, usable outside science itself? The big danger from the politicians and administrators or bureaucrats is the "master plan". Science cannot be planned from above. On the other hand you cannot do worthwhile research without looking and planning ahead.

A DIALOGUE

The only solution is a dialogue between scientists and the public, politicians and the administration. The dialogue must be based on the concept of accountability. Scientists use taxpayers' money and must be ready to explain and justify what they do. It must be based on an acceptance of the legitimate interests of society. The dialogue must be based on the inherent capacity for self-management in science and on knowledge about science. This dialogue is difficult. If it succeeds it will produce demands on science and the scientists. There will be calls for quality, competitiveness, international cooperation and relevance.

There is and has always been a conflict between the interests of science and the public. But there has also always been interdependence. We cannot eliminate the conflict, but we can stress the interdependence.

Finally, scientists often see the conflict as a question of freedom versus control. But the real choice has to be between freedom and competition, on the one hand, and control on the other. I am in favour of the first alternative. An example of this conflict is the story of the young coxcomb who told an elderly bureaucrat that "I want to fool around for a couple of years in the hope of discovering something by accident." The bureaucrat, however, replies with an old English proverb: "He who pays the piper, calls the tune."

REFERENCES

Cornford, F.M. (1908), *Microcosmographia Academia, Being a Guide for the Young Academic Politician*, Cambridge: Bowes and Bowes.

Robbins, C.B., Chairman (1963), *Higher Education. Report of the Committee Appointed by the Prime Minister on Higher Education*, London: Her Majesty's Stationery Office.

Thoren, V.A. (1990), *The Lord of Uranienburg: A Biography of Tycho Brahe*, Cambridge: Cambridge University Press.

CHAPTER 6

Science, the Public Purse and C.P. Snow

J. Meisel

It is highly appropriate to address the topic of "Science and the Public Purse" in the context of this gathering's return to C.P. Snow and his classic Rede Lecture, of forty years ago. Snow identified what Canadians, echoing the image imprinted on their minds by the title of Hugh MacLennan's famous novel (1945), like to call "two solitudes", after the chasm ascribed by the novelist to the relations between French-speaking and English-speaking Canadians. But Snow's solitudes, or cultures, as he called them, referred to the worlds of science and literature. Underlying this concern was a disenchantment with intellectuals in the humanities who, so C.P. Snow held, ignored or even disdained science and its actual and potential impact on society. He was preoccupied specifically with three threats: (i) thermonuclear war, (ii) the gap between the rich and the poor, domestically and throughout the world, and (iii) overpopulation.

Although his point of departure was science, Snow's apprehension focused on the societal dimension, on the broad impact of science. A one-time scientist, public servant, don and novelist, Snow was speaking as a *citizen*-scientist, preoccupied with the societal dimension, the impact of science on burning and threatening human problems having profound implications for society and politics. These, he surmised, were exacerbated by the dissonance between science culture and literary culture. His criticism of and malaise over the denizens of literary culture was a *cri de coeur* with respect to the need of the non-scientific world to respond to the challenges presented by science.

In his mind there was no distinction, at the time and in relation to his central preoccupation, between science and technology (S&T). These two sides of the same coin created the Industrial Revolution and thus fundamentally transformed the world. The word *revolution* was perfectly apposite, for the impact of S&T was to alter unrecognizably population patterns and movements, labour relations, landscapes and cityscapes and family relations, among other phenomena. And these changes led to profoundly troubling inequalities in income and life styles, both within Western Europe and globally, creating the growing tensions separating north and south countries. In a somewhat reckless act of aggregation, Snow identified the dominant elites with literary culture and accused them of wilfully ignoring the real problems confronting the world: the human condition in an era of cataclysmic technological transformation.

Specifically, the culprits were charged with not bothering to observe and understand what science did and of failing to address the consequences. Notably, the British ruling classes, at home and throughout the vast territories of the Empire and later the Commonwealth, neglected to place the issues arising from scientific and technological developments on the public agenda and to educate people so that they might be able to arrange their lives accordingly.

Snow's lecture invites the consideration of two massive conundrums: the then current state of the sociology of knowledge, with respect to his two cultures, and the socio-political consequences accruing from that state. His perspective focused on an extremely important aspect of the intellectual history of his times and rang a needed alarm. It is nevertheless essential to note that, from the perspective of someone living at the cusp of the twentieth and twenty-first centuries, it is strongly time and space specific. A Canadian reader, for instance, cannot but be struck by the profound differences between British social conditions prevailing at mid-century with those contemporaneously evident in Canada.

At the risk of appearing to be a country bumpkin from a land still burdened with a post-colonial mentality, I will consider one element in Snow's argument from a Canadian perspective. North America — Canada definitely included — never had and does not now have a literary class of the type identified by Snow with Britain. There are now a scientific community and a cultural community, very much larger than they were in the 1940s, but neither can be compared to the class conscious and aesthetically driven upper-middle level elite affecting public policy in the United Kingdom in Snow's time. If anything, Canadians, including its elites, have been at best indifferent and at worst hostile to intellectual and artistic pursuits (Meisel, 1998, 1999).

Were Snow to give the lecture now in a manner meaningful to a Canadian audience, he would have to counterpoise scientists to individuals identified not with a literary culture but to economists, marketeers, corporate princes and bean-counters — this is the dominant elite affecting public policy decisions.

All this, you may say, is very nice, but how does it relate to this chapter's theme, "Science and the Public Purse"? Very simply, comes the answer, quick as a shot. For the old adage, "He who pays the piper calls the tune" applies to this situation perfectly. This "patron" factor, is not, however, constant. It varies according to the identity of the instrumentalist and to the prevailing circumstances. These two elements determine what sort of interests are likely to be served by science.

At the first Herstmonceux conference in the current series, only four short years ago, the major problem for science, at least in Canada, was cutbacks in public spending. The principal piper (governments) had substantially turned down the tap and scientific work was consequently badly impaired (Meisel, 1998). By now some impressive improvements are under way but they still leave two major dilemmas, quite apart from the fact that the volume of supply is still, overall, meagre. The first dilemma concerns the organization of the science policy apparatus; a critical factor seemingly not apposite to our current topic. But, as we shall see, it is germane to our discussion. The second issue is central to our mandate: What tune is being called?

There are, of course, many. Some are atonal and grating, others melodic and pleasing. Among the latter, the federal government has either strengthened existing programmes or initiated new ones. The endowment of the Canada Foundation for Innovation has been increased to one billion dollars; in both 1998 and 1999 the budgets of the three granting councils (National Sciences and Engineering Research Council, National Research Council, Social Sciences and Humanities Research Council have been increased to unprecedented levels; the once temporary Networks of Excellence have been made permanent and the Medical Research Council is being enlarged and broadened into the Canadian Institutes of Health Research. Plans are also being considered for the creation of path-breaking Chairs in Research Excellence (Brzustowski, 2000*a, b*; Carty, 2000).

But while these and other recent developments indicate that the *scale* and *tempo* of scientific activity in Canada are almost certain to improve, there is no assurance at all that its *direction* will lead it toward salutary channels. The thunderous noise accompanying the introduction of every new or revised programme dwells almost exclusively on competitiveness (i.e., exports), job creation, technology transfers and partnerships between private, public and academic players. These goals are eminently worthy and it may seem churlish, to say the least, to quibble about them. Yet the heavy accent placed on them does cause anxiety and concern. It invites the question of which aspect of scientific work is excluded, neglected or ignored. The almost exclusive emphasis on *economic* benefits places the focus of research on short-run, applied and visible problems at the expense of more long-term, fundamental and theoretical issues. This sort of research target may inject hefty funding into scientific and technological innovation whose general benefit may be trivial. One example, taken from the private sector, is the two billion dollars allegedly spent by Gillette on the development of its Mach3 razor. There were, no doubt, some beneficial by-products but one cannot but wonder at the priorities of a society plagued by innumerably painful and deadly diseases whose treatments are under-researched, allocating billions to a minimally improved device for removing whiskers.

Still, it is only realistic to acknowledge that partnerships of university and government researchers with private interests can and do bring benefits. These arrangements often inject essential funds into the research community, diversify research sites and hence enhance the pluralism essential in a healthy scientific environment, and they also lead to a salutary marriage between theory and practice. So, to reject the new mood and mode entirely is misguided and counterproductive. Nevertheless, there are dangers involved which bear re-examination.

The participation of commercial or other profit-seeking interests in the research area usually involves a focus on quick, practical results bringing cash benefits to the firms involved. This, more often than not, is accompanied by a cautious, conservative outlook excluding the consideration of daring, "crazy" notions, wild hunches and the examination of unfashionable, remote topics. The history of discovery, however, attests to the colossal benefits, often even in commercial terms, of work of a purely theoretical, or seemingly airy-fairy kind.

Concern on the part of many thoughtful researchers and academic thinkers arises from the fear that the impetus for almost all moves in the science policy field, and hence in its funding, is virtually entirely economic. In some measure, the whole government apparatus is driven by the Department of Finance, Treasury Board and other economic ministers. It is significant and not accidental that science is under the Minister of *Industry*. The voice of the business community and of people besotted by an overwhelming and short-run conception of "the bottom line" is consequently heard at the exclusion of other tunes in the highest reaches of not only private but also of public decision-making bodies. Even measures and processes designed to ensure that the accountability and the fulfilment of the priorities of Parliament are realized are under the spell of this economic ethos. The key critical watchdog is called the Auditor General, although this office now surveys much more than the financial statements of the ministries and agencies of government. The public service has itself partly succumbed to self-serving mechanical procedures characterized by ever changing administrative fads, buzzwords, slogans and mumbo-jumbo mantras. Max Weber and other classic scholars of public service management would be more than a little confused by the bewildering succession of alleged panaceas invented and applied by modern practitioners: Program Policy Budgeting System, Zero-Based Budgeting, Management by Objectives, Total Quality Management, or Operational Performance Measurement System. In this jungle a dollar value is attached to everything done by the public service which is increasingly embracing a business ethos.

As a consequence, the *trahison des clercs* which Snow detected in the British cultural elites is perpetrated in Canada by economic elites both inside and outside the government, when the notion of "economic elites" refers to powerful people driven by economic goals. This obsession perforce obliges us to ask, since we are thinking of the public purse, whether the machinery of government is capable of ensuring that the piper's policy decisions are taken wisely and efficiently. And to respond realistically to that question, we need to ask another one: "Which piper?" There is not only the public-private dichotomy, but also the dimension imposed by Canada's federal system. What are and should be the respective responsibilities of Ottawa and the provinces, and what is the most beneficial relationship between them with respect to science policy? How important is it to aim at national standards and how much creative diversity can the system tolerate? The political context, including that imposed by federal and constitutional arrangements has an important effect on the capacity of governments to encourage scientific endeavours. Remember how former Quebec Premier Maurice Duplessis' view of the Canadian federation crippled scientific work and the *épanouissement* of universities in Quebec after the Second World War. A current scheme, the federal Millennium Scholarship Fund, in turn raises acute political conflict between Ottawa and Quebec. Similarly, the imposition of higher university fees on students from outside the province, as is currently done in Quebec, may hamper pan-Canadian efforts to enhance the scientific infrastructure.

The lesson to be taken from these observations is that, whatever the prevailing ideas and the discourse between groups and classes in society, the machinery of government is of primordial importance in determining even such seemingly remote matters as science policy and scientific activities. This is a dimension neglected by C.P. Snow in his "two cultures" argument. He expected that if the conundrum posed by the dissonance between science and literary culture was removed or at least diminished, the societal and political developments menacing humanity would be attenuated. He overvalued the capacity of science to address many of the ills afflicting humankind. A bookish man, despite his important stints in government, he discounted the degree to which the problems he found disquieting resulted from flaws in the administrative structure and in the folkways of the bureaucracy. This is astonishing in one whose novels often and realistically addressed issues of governance, and who spent much time in the Corridors of Power, to use a term he invented and immortalized in the title of one of his novels.

At the heart of the dilemma is the discouraging fact that scientists, scientifically informed literary people, *homo economicus*, social scientists and other experts cannot produce "correct" policies *on the basis of their special knowledge*. They can add rigour to the definition of issues, or sketch available options, but the policy decisions must come from the value system embedded in society. And the privileged means of articulating these values and of harmonizing them toward a widely accepted consensus is the political process. It is the system of parties and their interactions with the civil society and government institutions which in the end provide the means of laying down and applying the ground rules in an acceptable fashion. The public purse is required to provide the wherewithal for scientific activity and much of it must perforce come from government. It is therefore, not only the dissonance between the two cultures which affects society's problem-solving capacity, related to scientific issues, but also the arrangements affecting governance in general.

Scientists wishing to strengthen the performance of their craft by becoming involved in the public-policy process, a need of which the scientific community is at last becoming aware, must therefore seek not only to increase funding but also to enhance the quality of governmental decision-making with respect to science, and with the political process itself. Thus, how governmental decisions are reached, and broader issues like electoral reform, improvements in the functioning of the legislature and the public service, appropriate intergovernmental arrangements and a host of other things are highly relevant to science.

In short, the two cultures, even if they were to complement one another perfectly, are not sufficient to solve all societal problems. There are other cultures which are also pivotal.

It is both ironic and paradoxical that in C.P. Snow's "Strangers and Brothers" sequence of novels, many of these issues are brilliantly analyzed. Indeed one of the volumes, *The Masters*, is considered by some political scientists, as a truly virtuoso anatomy of politics, despite dealing with the selection of the new head of a Cambridge college.

REFERENCES

Brzustowski, T.A. (2000*a*), "The Role of Science in Public Policy: Some Observations", in *Statistics, Science and Public Policy: The Two Cultures?* ed. A.M. Herzberg and I. Krupka, Kingston: Queen's University, pp. 107-118.

———— (2000*b*), "Working with Canada's S&T Policy: Three Years of Learning", in *Statistics, Science and Public Policy: The Two Cultures?* ed. A.M. Herzberg and I. Krupka, Kingston: Queen's University, pp. 23-37.

Carty, A.J. (2000), "Canada's Policies and Investments in S&T: Where Do We Go from Here?" in *Statistics, Science and Public Policy: The Two Cultures?* ed. A.M. Herzberg and I. Krupka, Kingston: Queen's University, pp. 119-130.

MacLennan, H. (1945), *Two Solitudes*, New York: Duel, Sloan and Pearce.

Meisel, J. (1998), "Caesar and the Savants: Some Socio-Political Contexts of Science and Technology in Canada", in *Statistics, Science and Public Policy*, ed. A.M. Herzberg and I. Krupka, Kingston: Queen's University, pp. 153-177.

_____ (1999), "Science and the Public Trust", in *Statistics, Science and Public Policy: Science and the Public Trust*, ed. A.M. Herzberg and I. Krupka, Kingston: Queen's University, pp. 9-23.

CHAPTER 7

Shifting Cultures: The Role of Societal Support

M.E. Thompson

INTRODUCTION

I want to illustrate the influence of societal support on shifting cultures: the balance of strategic imperatives, the imperatives of the warriors and the victims, to use the terminology of Freeman Dyson (1984, ch. 1), and their impact on the academic imperative to understand (Table 1).

Table 1: Strategic Imperatives

warriors

- defence
- creation of wealth
- global competition

victims

- environmental preservation
- health and welfare
- social justice

Two manifestations of a new relationship between societal support and the academic enterprise: the noticeable evolution of traditional modes of support; and a more subtle manifestation contributing to cultural shifts, which I call the "intelligibility test".

What follows is a collage of quotations, with commentary, taken mainly but not entirely from the literature of Canadian funding programmes. If there are themes, they are the usual ones: that the priorities of the warriors are in ascendance, with strong implications for academic cultures; and that the new stronger engagement of society with the academic enterprise carries with it a sense of ownership which can be wonderfully beneficial but also constricting. But the reader may deconstruct at will!

BALANCE OF STRATEGIC IMPERATIVES

The new generation of warriors in the developed countries sees a strong analogy between making war and making money. The latter has gained in fascination, being more rewarding and personally fulfilling:

> Nowadays, CNBC has bureaus in London, Tokyo, and Hong Kong. 'We caught on to a Gulf War that's going to last forever. An event like this [stock market tumble] happens and Ron Insana becomes Norman Schwarzkopf', declared CNBC's president, Bill Bolster, "Talk of the Town" *(New Yorker*, October 1997).

> No doubt the boys in red suspenders have destabilized a government or two in the process. But by their intolerance for officially sanctioned lies, they have helped, not hindered, the cause of democracy. Currency speculators? Call them freedom fighters (Andrew Coyne, *Southam News*, November 1997).

As a cursory glance at any business section confirms, fascination with money goes along with fascination with the electronic media. The Canada Foundation for Innovation is an extremely important new federal programme which funds physical infrastructure for research: equipment, installations and libraries.

> The Canada Foundation for Innovation has earmarked up to $20M for a project to license the electronic delivery of scholarly periodicals to research university libraries across the country ... Some research libraries are still hopeful that a virtual research library, including books as well as

learned journals will exist in Canada in the not-too-distant future (*University Affairs*, March 1999).

The plan for a Canadian Institutes for Health Research (CIHR) has recently been launched with the federal budget, which also, on an interim basis, allocated an increase of $50 million per year for health research over the next three years to the granting councils and established programmes:

> An August 1998 poll conducted by Ekos Research found that the vast majority of Canadians attach great importance to health research. In fact, when asked about a variety of policy options, Canadians placed health research only slightly behind funding for medicare, and ahead of tax cuts and debt reduction, as their top choice for government action (First communiqué, Canadian Institutes of Health Research, November 1998).

The people responding to the August 1998 survey no doubt were thinking, "Maybe they'll find a cure for such and such a condition before it's too late for my mother, my brother, my child." In a more recent mission statement, the improvement of the health of Canadians is almost secondary to considerations of international competition and the synergy of health research and the economy:

> it is critical that Canada ensure global competitiveness for the funding of this innovative new enterprise ...

> Therefore, as a primary mission, the CIHR will facilitate investigator-initiated and discovery driven research that creates the new knowledge required to feed the innovation pipeline and improve the health of Canadians (The CIHR *Concept* http://www.cihr.org).

A plaintive note, sounded by a plant geneticist who studies the speciation of desert flora:

> At the announcement of provincial funding for UW [University of Waterloo] research on Monday, UW president James Downey remarked that 'After a period of relative drought, it can be said that the desert of academic research is beginning to bloom again.' Biology professor John Semple finds some irony in that analogy since, he says, 'As a consequence of over concern for "industrial partners" research by federal and provincial governments, there is an ever decreasing amount of funding for the study of deserts and things that bloom"(UW *Daily Bulletin*, March 17, 1999).

And indeed, the "strategic areas" of the granting councils, of which two are the Natural Sciences and Engineering Research Council (NSERC) and the Social Sciences and Humanities Research Council (SSHRC) are extremely wide ranging but quite anthropocentric (Table 2).

Table 2: Strategic Themes

NSERC – Biotechnologies
        – Energy Efficiency Technologies
        – Environmental Technologies
        – Information Technologies
        – Manufacturing and Processing Technologies
        – Materials Technologies

SSHRC – Challenges and Opportunities of a Knowledge-Based Economy
        – Society, Culture and the Health of Canadians
        – Exploring Social Cohesion in a Globalizing Era
        – Valuing Literacy in Canada

MODES OF SUPPORT

Another president and another professor, discussing donations: the engagement and the snaring, said that:

> [t]he thing with private support is that it's not just valuable for the funds it generates, but also for the process of accountability it engenders. Engaging with the individuals and communities that surround us causes us to become a better university (Robert Prichard, President, University of Toronto, Autumn 1997).

> This is the modern tension. The mediaeval scholar had to worry about the church.... We have to concern ourselves with the directing power of money. It's a seductive and driving influence (Bill Graham, President of University of Toronto Faculty Association, June 1998).

My own department has recently received a very large gift from a donor who insists on remaining anonymous and receiving no benefit from the donation. There are many donors who give large amounts to support institutional priorities out of altruism or gratitude, but not every large donor is content to be honoured with a scholarship, a lecture series, or a chair. Donor agreements increasingly use the language of partnership.

The older language of collaborative research and development and university/industry synergy is giving way as well, at least for now, to the language of partnership: public sector/private sector partnerships where both sides are equally engaged, leading to quantum jumps, simultaneously, in academic prowess and profitability. The Ontario Research and Development Challenge Fund (ORDCF), the agency concerned in President Downey's announcement, talks not of projects but investments:

> [we must get used to thinking of] the scholarly pursuit of truth alongside the pragmatic pursuit of profit (ORDCF spokesman, April 1999).

> If your vision does not exceed the complement of researchers and their excellent track records already in place, and if the investment by the ORDCF and your partners doesn't vault your institution into a pre-eminent position in their area, then you probably haven't got an opportunity whose vision encompasses the potential for high levels of excellence and impact (Open letter to ORDCF community, 1998).

The Social Sciences and Humanities Research Council has taken up the language of partnerships as well, with an emphasis on non-financial returns, and joint ownership of the research activities:

> Dr. Renaud [President of SSHRC] said that the new theme programmes will ... forge stronger linkages between university researchers, various communities and institutions — governments, for example — that need social sciences and humanities research expertise in order to craft policy and make decisions ... A key goal is to build interdisciplinary partnerships, bringing together the 'producers' and 'consumers' of research (SSHRC Website December 1998).

The new SSHRC Community-University Research Alliance (CURA) programme will actually receive applications jointly from universities and community organizations.

The latter will have not only a stake in the research, but a new kind of ownership.

THE INTELLIGIBILITY TEST

Perhaps the mathematicians feel the intelligibility test as acutely as any. A recent cartoon in the December 1998 issue of *The Emissary*, showing a mathematician being pelted by rotten tomatoes, has the caption "Let M be an ensemble of matrices with a measure μ ...".

Researchers are increasingly encouraged to explain their work in plain language, to make their work intelligible to the public and to the overseers of the funding programmes. In one way this is a very positive development, in that it reflects a public and political eagerness to become involved. But it can also be stifling. Very often, if research has reached the stage where it is ready to be made clear to a non-expert, it is essentially finished research. The intelligibility test cannot easily capture, except in retrospect, the creative throes at the beginning of research. I worry about this particularly in connection with new researchers. The application form for the Ontario Premier's Research Excellence Award (PREA), for new researchers, says only that a one hundred and fifty-word summary in plain language must be given. But the instructions for the first round of proposals given to our applicants internally went further:

> [The proposal] is not written for a committee of your peers as are proposals to NSERC/SSHRC/MRC. It will be reviewed first by civil servants in the Ministry ... then by the PREA Board ... generally the committee is composed of experts in bio-technology, engineering and information technology. Both of these groups of individuals should be regarded as intelligent generalists.... Therefore, the proposal *must* be written in general language that these individuals can understand (UW internal memo, 1998).

And the oral instructions went further still: "don't use technical terms or acronyms, try to tell a story that will capture the imagination." In later rounds, the intelligibility requirement has given way to an executive summary requirement, with applicants being asked to cut their detailed research proposals down from five pages to two!

The Canada Foundation for Innovation (CFI) has a standard application form, to be filled out by all, including new researchers applying for equipment under the new opportunities programme. For each of several categories, the applicant must choose a phrase from a menu of phrases, and take up to a page to justify the chosen phrase. The intention is to enable the application to be judged by non-experts:

The assessment section gives the applicant the opportunity to assess the project against each of the CFI criteria in a structured way, using the ProGrid^{TM} methodology, which is a combined application/evaluation tool.

ProGrid is a procedure for measuring the value of intangible assets, where precise numerical information is not available. It is a decision-assist tool customized to the needs of the CFI ... Reviewers will evaluate the merit of the project using the same methodology.

Seasoned applicants, somewhat cynically, appear to take this new kind of form in stride, but perhaps a new researcher, at the outset of a programme which could go anywhere, should be excused from this kind of exercise.

Apparently even the Natural Sciences and Engineering Research Council (NSERC) has been assaulted by the rotten tomatoes of the clamour for plain language once too often, as evidenced by this quote from the French edition of the most recent issue of *Contact*:

Just call us "En'serk" — spelled "NSERC" —

Even other federal departments have been known to get the English version of our name wrong ...

Ce texte n'a pas été traduit, car son contenu ne peut être compris que dans la langue de Shakespeare (CRSNG *Contact* Printemps 1999).

Further up in the text, francophone readers, members of the scientifically educated public, are told that they, like their anglophone counterparts, need no longer remember what the letters CRSNG mean.

But, of course, there is a more positive way of looking at that other academic imperative, the imperative to communicate, and I will let Allyn Jackson, a writer on mathematics, have the last word:

What do mathematicians hope to accomplish by influencing media coverage of their subject? If the hope is that increased media coverage will translate into increased financial support for mathematics, that hope might be misplaced. Consider the example of NASA, whose highly successful public relations organization captivated the nation with full-color footage of space exploration but whose budget has shrunk dramatically in recent years. Is celebrity the goal? It is hard to imagine that many mathematicians yearn for the harsh and fickle limelight accorded to celebrities today. Perhaps the aim is simpler: To edify the public about an important part of human culture. This is the most exalted and difficult goal of all. What it requires is a new orientation for media coverage of mathematics, one that makes a place for all the important developments in mathematics, not just the most easily explainable. It also requires mathematicians to think deeply about how to describe in plain terms why these developments are important. The media, with their new-found attention to mathematics, may well be ready to listen (*The Emissary*, December 1998).

REFERENCE

Dyson, F. (1984), *Weapons and Hope*, New York: Harper & Row.

PART IV

NATURAL AND SOCIAL SCIENCES

CHAPTER 8

Natural and Social Scientists: How Many Cultures?

Sir David Cox

C.P. Snow discussed two cultures, but surely there are more than two. Moreover, it is not clear how many dimensions are needed to describe the differences in a sensible way. I have no answer to this but want to make a few preliminary remarks about the relations between the natural and social sciences and the humanities.

The natural sciences can be thought of in a least three ways. First, there is science as an essentially ethical enterprise about improving understanding of the world. This is something perhaps less fashionable than it was a hundred years ago. For example, Karl Pearson (1906), writing an obituary of W.F. Weldon, said:

> but science no less than theology or philosophy is the field for personal influence for the creation of enthusiasm and for the establishment of ideals as self-discipline and self-development. If there is to be a constant stream of men who serve science from love, as men in greater religious epochs have served the church, then we must have scientific ideals of character (Pearson, 1906, p. 1).

Later he talked about "the single eyed devotion to the pursuit of truth".

Now it would be absurd to say that all natural scientists meet these high ideals and that there are not other people in many other disciplines who might feel similarly. But there is a question as to whether there is some useful special sense in which natural scientists have a distinguished ethical attitude connected in principle with open-mindedness and objectivity.

Secondly, there is science as a body of knowledge. C.P. Snow's emphasis on the second law of thermodynamics as a discriminator of scientists from non-scientists, suggests that he put a lot of weight on this idea. The structure of scientific knowledge is different from that of many other fields and consists of an enormous amount of detail held together by an ever-changing theoretical structure. Quantum mechanics is an example. As an outsider, it seems to me to be one of the most remarkable intellectual structures that man has discovered, although if one looks at its foundations it remains intensely controversial. The structure does not rest on its foundations in the usual sense.

Finally, there is science as method. Faced with a new problem, how do we design enquiries, collect data, analyze the data and so on? This is the aspect of most direct interest to statisticians.

Empirical social science uses some of the technology of science and the best social scientists are very careful about data quality, analysis and interpretation. In that sense, methodologically they are very like natural scientists. A key issue is whether there is a theoretical structure that holds the subject together. Economists may claim to have such a theory and other social scientists appeal to rational choice theory in the case of sociologists, and rational action theory in the case of political scientists. Both, and indeed the fundamental assumption of economics, are in a sense debased forms of statistical decision theory. Yet what distinguishes these from the theories of the natural sciences, is that in social science they may help explain retrospectively what has happened, they have had very little or no success in prediction. For example, I spoke recently to economists who specialized in the economy of South Korea and similar countries. Was the temporary collapse of these economies predicted? No. It can be explained retrospectively why it was obvious that the collapse would happen. That, while not to be totally dismissed, is much weaker than predictive success. Of course, I am concentrating on the empirical aspects of social science not on abstract theories.

King, Keohane and Verba (1999) in an important book, argued that the research methods used in the humanities and even the more descriptive parts of political science are not essentially different from those in science more broadly.

Nonetheless, there are undoubtedly differences not just in the nature of knowledge but in attitudes. One, for example, is the distinction between scholarship and research. Scholarship is knowing the literature of a subject inside out, a reverence for the written word of the past. Research is adding to the knowledge base, finding something that was not previously known; even the use of the word research is different in different fields, of course. Even in the natural sciences and mathematics there is a role for the fine scholar, the man who knows the literature well enough to find very specific and detailed information. That is scholarship. The researcher more highly prized in the sciences might say that this person knows the immediate literature of the highly specialized field, but is a bit vague at a more general level and is much more interested in pushing on and doing something new than in mastering the past.

For example, quotations are very rarely seen in scientific papers. In the humanities quotations abound and if they are from the ancient Greeks so much the better! Also there is a difference between various fields in the attitude to the philosophical base of one's subject. Many social scientists seem to have read the philosophers of science and even take what they read seriously. My impression is that most natural scientists get on and do what they have to do and disregard philosophy. This may sound like a slightly frivolous comment, but it is not totally so.

This discussion comes to no clear conclusion. There are many overlaps of attitude between natural science, social science and the humanities. The distinctions are more subtle than the idea of two cultures might suggest.

REFERENCES

Pearson, K. (1906), "Walter Frank Raphael Weldon, 1860-1906", *Biometrika* 5:1-52.
King, G., Keohane, R.O. and Verba, S. (1994), *Designing Social Inquiry: Scientific Inference in Qualitative Research*, Princeton: Princeton University Press.

CHAPTER 9

The Two Cultures: Forty Years Later

T.G. Flynn

It is now some forty years since C.P. Snow presented his Rede Lecture at Cambridge entitled "The Two Cultures and the Scientific Revolution". The view that Snow espoused about the gulf that he perceived as existing between the arts (exemplified by the "literary intellectuals" as he put it) and the natural scientists started a controversy which in the words of Stefan Collini was "remarkable for its scope, its duration and ... its intensity" (Collini, 1993, p. vii). It remained a topic of frequent discussion when I was a graduate student in the 1960s and was evident later as an undercurrent during meetings of the Faculty of Arts and Science at Queen's University. The gulf had not yet widened to yield the creation of separate Faculties of Arts and Science and perhaps to the university's credit still has not, but there is little, if any, interaction between scientists at Queen's and those in the arts at the professorial level and in that respect matters have not changed much since Snow's day. I suspect it is much the same at other universities. There are interpersonal social relationships among people in different disciplines, but in the main scientists and humanists and social scientists tend not to mingle and tend not to talk to one another in a substantive way.

To my mind the gulf still exists and is, perhaps, wider than ever. It is not, as Snow believed, a gulf between the literary intellectuals (by these Snow meant literary critics — a very small but influential group of literati) and natural scientists. It is, rather, a considerable gap in understanding between scientists and non-scientists and, is particularly evident between scientists and those in the humanities. This gulf can, however, be bridged by *mutually respectful communication* between the humanities and the sciences. Indeed, Snow himself clarified later (Snow, 1963) what he believed he had tried to convey in his lecture that "It is dangerous to have two cultures which can't or won't communicate". If there is mutual suspicion and incomprehension (Snow, 1959) between the two groups then it is because neither group has seen fit to develop a means of communication that leads to mutual respect and comprehension.

To Snow, a physicist, the world of natural science revolved largely around physics and the technology arising from physical laws such as in engineering and manufacturing. Snow was very concerned about the application of technology for the alleviation of worldwide problems, particularly those of the Third World, and he felt that the gulf between the two cultures was an impediment to solving the world's problems through technology. The technology to which Snow referred was much narrower in scope than is apparent today and a new science, which would give birth to a new technology, had already made itself known. Based somewhat in physics but more in genetics and biology the resulting science, molecular biology, and the technology it spawned would come to revolutionize natural science as much as physics had in the first half of the twentieth century. Not many outside those in biological science foresaw the immense consequences of the discovery of the double helix of DNA, arguably, the seminal event in molecular biology.

This discovery was made at Cambridge, not far from Snow's own stamping grounds at the Cavendish Laboratories and had been published in the journal *Nature* two years before the Rede Lecture. Snow, to his credit, in a second look at the two culture argument (Snow, 1963), recognized the importance of the double helix but even he, I think, would have been astonished at the impact that molecular biology, and its technological offspring biotechnology, has had on society. Stefan Collini in his introduction to the 1993 edition of *The Two Cultures* comments that "the development of molecular biology has probably been the most significant change in the face of science since the 1950s" (Collini, 1993, p. xlvii). There is no question that this is true and notwithstanding the very great fundamental advances made in theoretical physics, cosmology and astronomy in the last twenty-five years, these will not have the same impact on our everyday lives as will biotechnology.

The rapid advances made in biotechnology have of necessity brought to the fore the very real need for social responsibility in science and its applications. Since Snow's time the social sciences have developed enormously and the scientific study of human society and human relationships has become increasingly important in the evaluation of our daily lives. The broad range of modern technology brings science and scientists under the scrutiny of the politicians, the public and the ethicists as society tries to understand and place these technologies in the context of everyday life. The introduction of genetically modified plants is one of the more controversial examples that has, largely through scaremongering and ill-considered press reports, brought about hasty policy decisions by some governments. The fault does not lie with the public who are, by and large, not equipped with the knowledge necessary to make considered judgements; particularly when the information given is either too complex to understand or is presented in a select and sensational way by a press avid for news. The politicians also are ill-equipped to cope with technological information. Very few politicians are scientists or even have the faintest smattering of science and they are dependent on advisors for opinion. But often it seems that politicians react to prevailing public opinion with little expert advice. What then is the solution? The solution lies in closing the cultural gap so that the scientific revolution can be made comprehensible and decisions made in as informed and as rational a way as possible. How do we accomplish this? A good start would be for each side (the scientists and, for want of a better word, the humanists) to develop a mutual respect for each other's *ideas* and for the social scientists to make honest attempts to understand the *substance* of scientific discoveries before making pronouncements and conclusions about their implications. There has to be a mutually respectful dialogue.

The key to understanding any culture or discipline is two-fold. First, the culture has to be defined and second, the *language* used by that culture has to be understood. In regard to the first, science itself gets off to a bad start in that it is not even defined as a culture. The *Oxford Dictionary of the English Language* (OED) — and *Webster* for that matter — does not list science under the definition of culture. The primary entry under the heading "culture" in the OED defines it as "the arts and other manifestations of human intellectual achievement". Science is only mentioned under "the two cultures". It has to be agreed, therefore, that science *is* a cultural activity just as much as art, literature, music and any other of the humanities. It manifests human creative skills and certainly produces imaginative ideas. It is clearly an intrinsic part of our "customs, civilization and achievements" and should be accepted as such.

If it is accepted by the humanists that science is indeed a recogniz-able culture then the main objective on both sides should be an effort to understand each other's language. This is not easy. Let me give some examples which for scientists are so perplexing, yet so basic to an understanding of many of the humanities. The terms "modernism" and "post-modernism" are used frequently in the literature of art, architec-ture and literary criticism. To the scientist who, given the definition of modern in the *Oxford English Dictionary* as "of the present ... in cur-rent fashion", the concept of " post-modern" is baffling and illogical. Yet, recourse to the same source would clarify things and reveal that "modernism" refers to a whole range of individual artistic movements mostly in the first half of the twentieth century. Post-modernism is a late twentieth-century concept which has at its heart a departure from modernism, that is, those ideas that were in vogue at a much earlier time. Of course, these definitions are in no way an in-depth explana-tion, but they do lend some clarification. They help enormously in trying to understand the context of much that concerns the humanist and the social scientist. I doubt very much that many scientists have taken the time to even look up these concepts in the dictionary. How-ever, in my experience not many social scientists have taken the trou-ble to explain the context in which they work. There is an inability and unwillingness to communicate that lends little credit to either side. Problems in communication rarely occur when ideas are transmitted to colleagues in the same or cognate disciplines. Problems occur when there is a need to communicate with a broader audience and members of a particular culture or discipline fail to do so. The worst aspect of this is when one culture does not make the effort or does not see the need to communicate with the non-*cognoscenti*. Both scientists and humanists are guilty of a considerable arrogance in this regard.

The recent furore in Great Britain and Europe over genetically modi-fied foods is a good example of rush to judgement resulting from extremely poor communication between the scientists and the public. The first mistake made was an inability to communicate the nature of genetic modification in a simple and comprehensible way. Not that it is easy to do this. Most non-scientists have only a very vague idea of what a gene is, let alone the make-up of a gene. The press and the public talk very glibly about the nature of the substance that make up genes, that is, DNA but the word "deoxyribosenucleic acid" (DNA) is incomprehensible. Similarly, the everyday phraseology of the molecular biologists such as 2-D gel electrophoresis and polymerase chain reaction and the quarks, mesons and besons of the physicists are equally mysterious. And what is the general public and the social scientist to make of the idea of prions and their role in mad cow disease and Creutzfeldt-Jakob disease in humans when scientists themselves are not entirely sure about the cross-species transmissibility of prion-involved diseases?

For all issues involving the implications of modern science, opinion has to be informed. Scientists must take the time to present scientific ideas in a comprehensible way and social scientists and humanists must undertake an effective dialogue with the scientists so that there is mutual understanding of the implications of scientific discovery. Neither side should take it on themselves to become the final arbiter and present conclusions to either the politicians or the public.

There are many cultural elements of civilized society which make life worth living. Science is one of them. The gulf that exists between science and the other cultures must be bridged by mutual understanding and respect.

REFERENCES

Collini, S. (1993), "Introduction," to *The Two Cultures* by C.P. Snow, Cambridge: Cambridge University Press.

Snow, C.P. (1959), *The Two Cultures and the Scientific Revolution*, Cambridge: Cambridge University Press.

_____ (1963), "The Two Cultures: A Second Look," *The Times Literary Supplement*, October 25.

CHAPTER 10

On Snow and After

F.K. Hare

I belong to the large contingent of scientists who have read C.P. Snow's Lewis Eliot novels and enjoyed them; but who did not understand what so annoyed F.R. Leavis, whom I had never read until he attacked Snow. I did not attend the Rede Lecture in 1959, nor did I pay much attention to the fuss raised by Leavis' subsequent attacks.

Snow was certainly right in asserting in the Rede Lecture (Snow, 1959) that a gulf did exist then between the two cultures he chose to define, though I do not think it was uniform across the industrialized world. The situation is now different. I can only write impressionistically about the changes. I do not like unsupported assertions, but I cannot claim to have established anything by critical analysis. I can only hand-wave.

I am struck by Snow's misjudgements about the future. He assailed, for example, Britain's tradition of specialized education, which I had always seen as a source of strength. He regarded specialization as an analogue of entropy. "...we are only capable," he said, "of increasing specialisation, not decreasing it" (Snow, 1959, p. 19). But shortly thereafter a rash of liberalization infected the British universities, freeing up the curriculum without, in my view, adding anything to its value or quality. And he entirely misjudged the relative strengths of the U.S. and USSR systems of education. "Here, unless and until the Americans and we educate ourselves both sensibly and imaginatively, the Russians have a clear edge," he wrote (ibid., p. 45). However, he threw a lifeline: "Russia is catching up with the U.S. in major industry — but it will be a long time before Russia is as convenient a country as the

U.S. in which to have one's car break down" (ibid., p. 42). Here at least he was right.

Any former student could just as easily jibe at me for my own ventures into socio-economic forecasting. I am not making fun of Snow, but of all of us: the future is always a surprise, and futurists live largely in vain. I cannot resist, however, pointing to one more miscall in Snow's lecture. In dealing with the rich and poor nations, he argued that it would take a long time for Third World nations to catch up in the scientific revolution. He said it took Russia forty years to make the jump, and that the Chinese might well get there in only half the time. But Japan was not mentioned at all. Imagine overlooking Japan in 1959!

Where he did score a "bull's-eye" was in seeing that the electronic revolution would transform the world's economy: "[It] is in cardinal respects different in kind from any that has gone before," he wrote, "and will change the world much more" (ibid., p. 28). This, he insisted, was the true scientific revolution. I do not agree with him; I would put the date of the scientific revolution when the flow of ideas between science and technology were largely reversed. The earlier industrial revolution was led, not by scientists, but by brilliant craftsmen like Abraham Darby and the Wedgwoods. From about Faraday on, however, truly scientific ideas began to generate new technologies. The modern phase to which Snow refers was started when the semiconductors and transistors arrived, and made electronics fundamental to industry, communications and even household devices. Nevertheless, Snow was basically right: automatic control of human devices, combined with almost magical communications, has changed our lifestyle, mostly for the better; though I confess that automated bank tellers and press-button routines on the telephone drive me up the wall — as does having to learn how to type, so that I can send e-mail.

A point made by Freeman Dyson suggests even more profound consequences (Dyson, 1998). The revolution in modern biology and communications made possible by ultra-high-tech devices has made the scientific laboratory a training ground for ultra-high technologists and technicians (if they are any longer separable). People trained in the leading laboratories have taken back their skills in making such devices into the industrial setting. It used to be ideas that flowed (for example, from Faraday and Maxwell to Edison and Marconi). Now it is also people. Technologists who know how to manipulate the DNA molecule, and can develop devices to do so, move freely into the biotechnology industry. The same is true *a fortiori* in the communications and space technology trades. Pure and applied science interdigitate as never before.

Has this sea change affected Snow's vision of two separate cultures, the one literate and other numerate? It certainly has in Britain, the United States, and that often-forgotten land, Canada; and, of course, across all of Europe and parts of Asia. I was Provost of Trinity College Toronto (from 1979 until 1986), traditionally a haven for the humanities and theology. During those years there was a rising clamour for access to word processors on the part of both faculties; and the library went through an electronic revolution. The serious press in North America usually adds e-mail or WWW addresses to articles, and most columnists are only available by such means. I am not aware that Peregrine Worsthorne, Auberon Waugh and W.F. Deedes have joined the club, but they will have to.

Of course, use of the WorldWideWeb and the Internet does not in itself indicate a *rapprochement* of the two cultures; the new things are at present a cult, a fashion and toys as much as they are a means of dissemination of facts, fancies, lies, pious hopes, hatreds and whatever. But awareness of high technology, and of the extraordinary dividends to be earned from uncensored, freely accessible information and comment, have penetrated most people's consciousness. In North America there is no longer a cosy place in which the literate culture can insist on dominating the various national lives, if it ever did. I believe the same to be true in Britain and Ireland.

On the other hand, I see few signs that the scientific community wants to broaden its perspective toward the more literate parts of our culture. *Science*'s recent series of opinion pieces on this subject is a step forward, and I know that Sigma Xi has highly liberal intentions. But few of my colleagues read the modern equivalents of Kafka. As in Snow's time, the natural artistic bent of the scientist is toward music and Bach is still "top of the pops".

What can one say about the recent public success of books usually called popularizations of science? Do they represent a mass movement of interest toward science among adults, interest among the young having waned in many countries? The sales of *A Brief History of Time* have been astounding, and cannot simply be a mark of respect for Hawking's refusal to be silenced by illness (Hawking, 1988). What accounts for the enthusiasm for Penrose's very difficult *The Emperor's New Mind*? (Penrose, 1990) or E.O. Wilson's *Consilience*? (Wilson, 1998). These are excellent books by brilliant scholars. But I find them tough to read, after years of exposure to the research world. I would say that they are evidence of two vital things: that high attainment in pure science does not rule out practical literacy among its front-runners; and that a large, well-intentioned audience exists outside high science for such books. That, I suspect, would have amazed Snow.

Does this argument have anything to do with the way the world actually runs? I would say "not much", as Snow might have done. Though the material and communications aspects of life are based in science and engineering, the houses of Parliament and board-rooms are still dominated by lawyers, accountants and professional managers. In schools of business, management studies flourish. And the social pecking order seems dominated by income, not inherited wealth. Few scientists want to become involved, because the conduct of public affairs involves artifices, ethics and skills that simply do not interest most of my scientific colleagues.

In effect, the world of business and politics likes to employ scientists to apply their findings, and to accept their judgements on technological questions. But that world does not incorporate scientists into the highest decision-making levels, because most scientists do not insist on being there. And if they did arrive in any numbers, I suspect that they would make as big a mess of running things as do the lawyers, accountants and senior bureaucrats. Shrewd qualitative judgement goes with no particular training, and may well be just luck.

I recently witnessed a good example of how things can go wrong in a free society, the fall from grace of one of the world's great public utilities, Ontario Hydro. Twenty years ago it was admired worldwide, and was in the midst of an even greater expansion, based on nuclear power and on the assumption that the demand for electric power would increase exponentially for years to come. Today, a significant fraction of its nuclear capacity is out of production for a prolonged rehabilitation program, led by trouble-shooters from the United States, and there is no plan for further expansion. The monopoly on which it depended has been broken, and a neo-conservative government has disaggregated the megalithic corporation, just as British Rail and the Central Electricity Generating Board have been carved up in Britain. Costs are mounting, though prices are frozen. Morale among the highly-talented staff has plummeted. The talent is still there, but the motive is not. And public safety, though still intact, has at best not been increased.

How do these things happen? Why do large enterprises tend to destroy themselves? Why did the University of London not prosper, even though some of its colleges were superb? Why did even IBM falter? We are witnessing an extraordinary move, called globalization, whereby giant conglomerates are becoming bigger by swallowing their weaker competitors worldwide. Amazingly, this is seen as a sign of vitality. The phenomenon is most apparent in those fields where electronic communications have been joyously applied. I am not clever enough to say whether this process is really for the collective good or the selective bad. But I fear that we shall soon be re-reading the parable of the Gadarene swine. Everything in my experience suggests that growth in size is *not* the way to public good; it is elephantiasis.

None of this emerges from Snow's Rede Lecture. And no good answers have yet asserted themselves elsewhere. So what do we do? My own answers are to let science go its way; to make as much good use of its findings as we can, and to diagnose the genuine ills of our contemporary world, which is, I am sure, mortally ill.

Individually we are all mortal, as Keynes so elegantly pointed out. But collective survival for humanity and the rest of nature call for an understanding far beyond Snow's — and, so far, beyond all of us. We live in times when pundits can still make a good living pretending they know otherwise. They escape with their emoluments before their fallibility is made obvious. Unfortunately some of their errors are taken seriously, and are in part self-fulfilling in consequence. I would suggest a prolonged dose of the nostrum on which all science depends, scepticism!

REFERENCES

Dyson, F.J. (1998), "Science as a Craft Industry", *Science* 280:2048-2049.
Hawking, S.W. (1988), *A Brief History of Time: From the Big Bang to Black Holes*, New York: Bantam Books.
Penrose, R. (1990), *The Emperor's New Mind*, London: Vintage.
Snow, C.P. (1959), *The Two Cultures and the Scientific Revolution: The Rede Lecture 1959*, Cambridge: Cambridge University Press.
Wilson, E.O. (1998), *Consilience: The Unity of Knowledge*, New York: Knopf.

CHAPTER 11

Two Cultures or One?

D.B. McLay

C.P. Snow delivered the Rede Lecture, "The Two Cultures and the Scientific Revolution" to a Cambridge audience in May 1959. An expanded version, *The Two Cultures and a Second Look*, was written by Snow in 1963 after the first edition had been reprinted ten times during 1959-62, partly in response to the ferment generated by F.R. Leavis' vitriolic counter-attack "Two Cultures? The Significance of C.P. Snow", delivered as the Richmond Lecture at Cambridge in February 1962, and printed by *The Spectator*, March 9, 1962. The controversy stimulated many commentaries in the 1962-64 period (Cornelius and St. Vincent, 1964).

During 1956-62, as a young assistant professor in New Brunswick and a participant in many informal and interdisciplinary discussions, I read Snow's lecture and was not impressed by it, mainly because the polarization between humanists and natural scientists that marked "High Table" at Cambridge was not apparent at the University of New Brunswick. Nor had I detected any such animosity during my undergraduate days at McMaster University in Hamilton where each science student was required to take a number of courses in the humanities and social sciences in order to fulfil the degree requirements. My professors of history and philosophy taught me far more about the historical development of the sciences than did any of my professors in chemistry and physics. My experience in two institutions of higher learning in British Columbia in the 1951-56 period was also totally inconsistent with C.P. Snow's assessment of the rift between the "two cultures".

Snow introduced two touchstones for the understanding of science by humanists — the description of the second law of thermodynamics and an awareness of the 1957 discovery at Columbia University of the breakdown of the conservation of parity. With respect to the latter, the majority of scientists outside chemistry, mathematics and physics do not have a clue about the role of parity in quantum mechanics let alone the discovery of non-conservation in so-called "weak interactions". All research in chemistry and much of that in physics can be conducted without attention to the non-conservation of parity in ß-decay. With respect to thermodynamics, it has been my experience that many students of engineering have trouble understanding the second law. Senior undergraduates in physics only begin to understand the second law after they have learned Boltzmann's definition of entropy in a course on statistical mechanics. Philip Morse, a theoretical physicist at the Massachusetts Institute of Technology, wrote a book, *Thermal Physics*, for very bright senior students majoring in physics, mathematics and engineering. In the introduction to his book, Morse states: "In fact, because it does not make use of atomic concepts, thermodynamics is a rather abstract subject, employing sophisticated concepts, which have many logical interconnections; it is not easy to understand one part until one understands the whole"(Morse, 1965, p. 4). In his chapter on the second law in the 1962 preliminary edition, he notes: "The enunciation of the second law is also roundabout; its various paraphrases are many and, at first sight, unconnected logically." In the 1965 corrected edition, Morse adds: "So we cannot schedule our discussion of the second law as we do with other theories in physics, starting with a few crucial experiments, and building the theory up in an obviously inductive manner from the empirical facts" (ibid., p. 47). Even the celebrated theoretical physicist Erwin Schrödinger, in his influential lectures delivered at Dublin in 1943 with the title *What is Life?* presented fallacious concepts of "negative entropy" and of the violation of the second law in living organisms; he neglected the requirement that the second law should apply only to closed systems. In short, not only was Snow grossly unfair to his colleagues in his requirement that they be able to describe the second law of thermodynamics, but his fixation on this test casts doubt on his own scientific judgement.

Students of the humanities may not be able to grasp the excitement of physicists in their search for the "Higgs boson" as part of the confirmation of the "standard model" of particle physics but they are interested in particle accelerators, thermonuclear fusion, the formation of galaxies and other aspects of particle physics and astrophysics. They are also very much concerned with topical issues such as global warming, ozone depletion, environmental pollution and genetic manipulation. It is interesting to note that David Levy, the co-discoverer of Comet Shoemaker-Levy 9 that crashed spectacularly into Jupiter in 1994, gained his interest in astronomy from writing his M.A. thesis on the mystical views expressed in the poems of Gerald Manley Hopkins. A friend began her study of astronomy while she was a student at the Ontario College of Art. She went on to take her Ph.D. in astrophysics and now after several post-doctoral fellowships is working in Baltimore on "visualization" of the signals from the Hubble Space Telescope. Many art historians have become interested in the diagnostic capabilities of such discoveries in physics as proton-induced X-ray emission, infrared reflectography, laser-induced fluorescence and thermoluminescence. Some physicists have recently become fascinated with the "anamorphic art" found in the works of such Renaissance artists as Hans Holbein and Leonardo da Vinci.

Both the humanities and the natural sciences have been challenged intellectually by the French currents of deconstructionism and post-structuralism with their arcane vocabularies and indigestible verbiage. It appears that these movements are in decline, but in the previous decade they caused great schisms in departments of history, literature and philosophy. A new and growing challenge is the current emphasis on the part of governments, granting bodies and university administrations on the commercial benefits of university research. One wonders what Schrödinger, a devotee of the theatre as well as a philosopher and poet, would have thought of contract research, patenting of intellectual property and technology transfer. And yet his wave equation, discovered during a Christmas vacation in the Swiss Alps, is the basis, along with the statistics of Fermi and Dirac, for an understanding of semiconductor electronics. Dr. Gerhard Herzberg, Nobel laureate in chemistry and an early supporter of these Herstmonceux conferences, stated during the opening of Stirling Hall at Queen's University on May 14, 1965: "scientific research of the purest kind is an intellectual activity which just like art, music, literature, archaeology, and many other fields, helps us to understand who we are and what is the nature of the world in which we live." At his memorial service in Ottawa in May 1999, those attending not only heard of these ideals but also heard recordings of his singing of baritone solos from Faust and Iolanthe as recognition of his passion for great music. Sir Denys Wilkinson, Vice-Chancellor Emeritus of Sussex, on the occasion of a convocation address at the University of Saskatchewan on November 6, 1964 said:

"And so we delight in physics for the same reason that we delight in the arts, because it makes us feel good inside and because it takes us further along the endless road that is ours alone, the realization of Man as Man."

Dr. Alfred Bader holds a Ph.D. in organic chemistry but his real passion has been the acquisition of seventeenth-century Dutch paintings. Of these, he has written: "My enjoyment of paintings has taken me searching in beautiful estates and tiny garrets, into great auction houses and flea markets. I love discoveries, not only of material value, but of great beauty. And getting to know the people involved in art has enriched my life" (Bader, 1995, p. 227).

REFERENCES

Bader, A. (1995), *Adventures of a Chemist Collector*, London: Weidenfeld and Nicolson.
Cornelius, D.K. and St. Vincent, E. (1964), *Cultures in Conflict: Perspectives on the Snow-Leavis Controversy*, Chicago: Scott, Foresam.
Morse, P.M. (1965), *Thermal Physics*, New York: W.A. Benjamin Inc.

CHAPTER 12

Two Cultures: The Unnatural Nature of Science

L. Wolpert

There is a concern with the public understanding of science. A university professor of geography assigns the following problem to his geography students. They are asked whether the following chemical should be banned. The chemical industry routinely uses the chemical dihydrogenmonoxide in its processes; it is often used in significant quantities; it leads to spillages and other leaks; and it can regularly find its way into rivers and food supplies. This chemical is known to have the following environmental effects: it contributes to acid rain; causes erosion; damages automobile brakes; and in its vapour state, is a major greenhouse gas. It has been found in the tumours of all terminally ill patients; it can cause excessive sweating and vomiting and accidental inhalation can kill. Should this chemical be strictly regulated or even banned by an authority such as the government of the United Kingdom or the European Union? Half of his class voted to ban the use of water.

A quotation from D.H. Lawrence illustrates some of the hostility to science from the arts. "Knowledge has killed the sun making it a ball of gas with spots.... The world of reason and science, this is the dry and sterile world the abstracted mind inhabits" (quoted in Wolpert, 1992). Why is there this confusion and hostility?

This paper was delivered as the speech following the banquet.

The answer partly lies, I think, in C.P. Snow's idea of the two cultures. The concept of the two cultures did raise a very important issue — science is different from the arts. I am, however, not impressed by Snow. I think he is a dull writer in that particular essay, and is a terrible snob. That whole essay is about Oxbridge. It is as if there is no other world; as if the only serious issue is that at High Table, the literary people do not take scientists seriously; as if there are only two cultures: the literary people and the scientists. Lawyers, butchers, farmers, journalists? They do not exist. I also find unacceptable his put-down of biology, "Not much intellectual effort to understand this. Any, any, any painter or sculptor could understand crystallography without any difficulty whatsoever."

Nevertheless, the "two cultures" has become an extremely important idea. In fact, had Leavis not been so nasty about Snow, the "two cultures" would not have received the publicity it has. The disappointing part of Snow's analysis is the shallow understanding of what underlies the two cultures divide. He just does not analyze it. He does, however, put his finger on a very important problem and that is what is special about science.

In my own experience, my non-scientific friends have enormous difficulty with science. For example, I was on a television programme with a distinguished British commentator, and I was saying, "look, cloning is a lot of fuss about nothing", and he said, "but someone will make lots of little Hitlers." I replied, "but who will the mothers be and where will they go to school?" "Mothers," he said, "what on earth has cloning to do with mothers?" This is a common experience. When individuals think about cloning, they think clones just arrive from the test tube as it were and no pregnancy is involved.

Non-scientists do have difficulty with science and I was particularly struck by a comment by Lionel Trilling, a distinguished American literary critic, who said that he recognized that science was probably one of the greatest intellectual achievements of the age, but he did not understand it at all. He found it extremely difficult and he was humiliated by this.

When I began to think about why this should be, I came up with the realization that science really is peculiar, and it is so for a number of reasons. And one of the main reasons is that the world is not built on a common-sense basis. It is nobody's fault. Science does not fit with common sense. By common sense, I mean one's natural expectations about the way the world works. Any sensible person, when eventually the sun appears in summer in Britain, concludes that the sun goes round the earth. This is what I mean by one's natural expectations. If I tell people that only 70 per cent of the people in Britain believe that it is the earth that goes around the sun and not the other way round, my audience usually laughs knowingly. However, if I ask them for their evidence that the earth does go around the sun and not the other way round, silence usually falls. I have been to the Astronomer Royal and asked for a simple way of explaining the evidence of the earth going around the sun — this is difficult. Another physicist replied by saying, "it is obvious why it is, how can you be so stupid?" It is a question of conservation of momentum. The sun is big, the earth is small, obviously the earth will go around the sun. But for the public this is not at all obvious. So I strongly state: any idea that anybody has that fits with a common-sense expectation about the way the world works will be wrong scientifically. There are thousands of examples, such as tides. Everybody says the moon causes the tides; the moon pulls on the water so it is high tide on the opposite side. Even Galileo struggled with that problem and could not get it right.

Some of my critics say that I put people off science by calling it unnatural. But many non-scientists say they now understand why they found science so difficult. They expected it to fit with natural expectations; it was quite a relief to know that it does not.

It is also essential in understanding the nature of science to distinguish between science and technology. Science is about understanding the way the world works, technology is about actually making things, sometimes about putting science into practice. History supports this. Science had virtually no impact on technology until the late eighteenth century. The steam engine owed nothing to science. The great buildings of the Renaissance were built on what has been called the Five-Minute Theorem: you put up the building, you take away the props, you wait for five minutes and if it is still standing, you assume it is going to last forever. And, of course, lots of them fell down. It was imaginative trial and error and that is a very powerful way of doing technology. Early agriculture and the isolation of metals owed nothing to science. But medicine was based on Galenic science and people were bled to death for two thousand years. The proof that you can have amazing technology without science is evidenced by the elephant. I claim that the elephant is a remarkable technology, but evolution knows no science, just trial and error.

My other evidence to support the idea that science really is peculiar is the fact that it only happens once in history. One can make a very strong case that only one society ever came across the idea of doing science and that is the Greeks, and all science as we know it comes from the Greeks. What about the Chinese? The Chinese, as Joseph Needham makes absolutely clear, did not have science. They were amazing technologists, with a much more mystical approach. They had nothing equivalent to Greek science.

If one is interested in the public policy and public understanding of science, I think it may be helpful to recognize that science does have these peculiar aspects. As well, while actually doing science, one has to adopt a rigour and an internal consistency that may be true of other academic disciplines but is much more rigorous in science. It is also very mathematical in parts. Having said that science is peculiar, one might have thought that those people who professionally spend their lives studying science as science, namely the philosophers of science and the sociologists of science, will have something terribly interesting to tell us about science; alas not. For scientists and non-scientists, philosophy of science in this century has contributed nothing to the understanding of the special features of science and how it works. The sociologists of science, the relativists who have obscured the nature of science, are essentially anti-science as they regard it as nothing more than a cultural construct of no particular validity.

Can one bring the two cultures or even the many cultures together? What about the arts? It is very fashionable at the moment to emphasize the similarity between arts and sciences. Jacob Bronowski argued that creativity in art and creativity in science are one and the same thing. This is both sentimental and snobbish. It is saying that scientists are really artists, just doing something slightly different and the artists can say that their creativity is just like that of the scientists. If anyone had said that the way accountants do their work is creative in exactly the same way as artists or scientists then I would be more impressed. I think it is very important to bring the arts and sciences together, but by conflating them and pretending that they are similar is to miss the essential features of both. There is an important statement by the mathematician David Hilbert, who said the measure of a good scientific paper is how many other papers it makes irrelevant. You cannot say that of the arts. There is progress in science, but only change in the arts.

The related feature is that ultimately the individual in science is irrelevant. Let me offer you the following scenario: go back, say a thousand years, and science is run again with a different group of people: given an intelligent group of people with enough money and time, water will turn out to be H_2O, DNA will be the genetic material, the cell will be the basic unit of life and while I do not know enough about particle physics, it will also be the same. Brilliant individuals speed up things but science is a collective, and, though we honour individuals, give them prizes, and name things after them, ultimately they are irrelevant because their contribution becomes part of a general body of knowledge. It is the opposite in the arts: no Shakespeare, no Hamlet, no Macbeth, no Lear. When a modern writer writes a play, it does not make anything else irrelevant as Shakespeare never made anything else irrelevant.

So, this idea that we are all part of the same creative group diminishes both art and science. The Wellcome Trust devotes a significant amount of money to bringing the visual arts (incidentally, the visual arts is a word that never even enters Snow's vocabulary) together with science. But one of the curious things about the visual arts is that they require the least intellectual effort to appreciate them. Tens of thousands of people went and enjoyed the Monet exhibition in London recently. An intellectual background is not necessary to appreciate the beauty of Monet. Compare it with science. I just about understand the second law of thermodynamics, but I am sure it is beautiful; the genetic code may be beautiful, but to appreciate beauty in science requires a great deal of knowledge. By pretending it is all the same, one loses the important ideas and deludes the artists into thinking that they understand science and this becomes a misguided enterprise. One should bring arts and sciences together in order to have each understand the other, and understand the differences at the same time.

Have things really changed since Snow put forward his ideas? Have, over the last forty years, the two cultures come closer together and do people have a better understanding of science? If at all, just a little. But you may argue that there are all those wonderful and popular science books, which everybody reads in very large numbers. I think many are read as magic. It is often not about science as understanding, it is science as magic. When people are fascinated by chaos, for example, it may not be because people are interested in science but because chaos is a magical idea. I often think if only Heisenberg had not called his important discovery "The Uncertainty Principle"; if he had given it a nice technical name, people would not have forever been using it or abusing it in the way they do. It is the magic of science. To capture a television audience in the United Kingdom, you need to put on something related to the paranormal.

If literature is meant to, as it were, reflect the society in which the writers live, then we live largely in a society in which there are no female scientists. There are middle-aged, boring, emotionally deprived and dangerous men doing science. You will hunt with some difficulty — there are exceptions such as the doctor in George Eliot's *Middlemarch* — to find a single positive image of science in English literature. Carl Djerassi, who invented the birth control pill, has started to give some sort of description of science in his novels but that is only recently. If one looks back at what literature has done for science, it has been a disaster. Mary Shelley, author of *Frankenstein*, is the unintentional evil fairy godmother of genetics. It is impossible to discuss genetics without having the image of Frankenstein. In the recent hysteria over genetically modified foods they have been called "Frankenstein foods". *Brave New World*, the Island of Dr. Moreau and Hollywood have embraced this idea with enormous enthusiasm.

There is another problem. This, I feel, is probably the most serious problem in relation to science and the young. We live in an age where personal expression, or expressing one's own views, is terribly important. Anybody can have a view about a poem or a novel. I am afraid that your views on my ideas about developmental biology are not relevant. Science does not offer someone outside a particular field the opportunity to have a personal view. My students cannot have a view about how embryos develop in the same way that they can have a view about ideas on the origins of the French Revolution, or about a particular poem. And I think this is really quite hard for school children. I imagine children feel that they have something to contribute at all levels in the humanities. But in relation to science, this is not so, as there is an enormous amount of knowledge needed before a comment becomes useful. The mathematician, Christopher Zeeman, told me that you really only vaguely begin to know what research in mathematics is about in about the second year of a Ph.D.

It is essential to find out what is known before even a tiny contribution to science can be made, and this presents a very real problem. These things are neither good nor bad. It is just the way the world works. Scientific knowledge, value-free and reliable, is neither good nor bad. It is the best way to understand the world and I think that we should cherish its special features and not try to conflate them with other aspects of other cultures.

REFERENCE

Wolpert, L. (1992), *The Unnatural Nature of Science*. London: Faber & Faber.

PART V

SCIENCE AND PUBLIC POLICY

CHAPTER 13

The Role of Science in Public Policy: Some Observations

T.A. Brzustowski

INTRODUCTION

This paper is about science and public policy. It offers some observations about the role of science in developing and implementing public policy. My perspective is that of someone with a background of university research in engineering who has subsequently worked in government for a dozen years. The object is to better understand the nexus of science and policy, and particularly to develop a clearer view of the role of government scientists in the formulation of government policy. The motivation for such an attempt came from my discomfort in watching the recent public disputes between scientists in two government departments[1] and their employer. Perhaps a better mutual understanding of how scientists do science and how governments make policy might prevent future disputes of this kind. This paper is offered as a step in that direction.

TWO CULTURES AT WORK

My first observation is that superficial perceptions and imprecise language bedevil the relationship. That should not be a surprise. The scientific community and the policy community generally, in Canada at least, are people with entirely different, if not mutually exclusive, educational backgrounds; for all intents and purposes, C.P. Snow's two cultures. They have different values, they use language differently, they employ different paradigms to aid their understanding of the world, and they are accustomed to dealing with very different kinds of issues. Scientists analyze, and policy-makers synthesize. They deal differently with correlation and causality. Their perceptions of each other's role in the policy process, and sometimes even of their own, are not always accurate. For example, some policy-makers wrongly expect science to produce certainty. On the other hand, some scientists wrongly consider politics a pejorative, an inappropriate consideration in making public policy that involves science. It does not help when scientists claim that their research is producing policy prescriptions, or when policy-makers do not distinguish between a serious scientific dispute and mainstream scientific criticism of junk science. Policy is an area where C.P. Snow's two cultures have to work together, and the big challenge is to build a bridge of understanding between them.

In what follows, I shall discuss three aspects of the science-policy nexus: scientific fact, scientific prediction and the positioning of scientific advice in the process of making public policy.

SCIENTIFIC FACT

Some questions of public policy can be answered only with a finding established by the scientific method, verified repeatedly and independently, and accepted as fact by the scientific community. For brevity, I shall call that a scientific fact. The process of establishing a scientific fact is illustrated in Figure 1. Acceptance of a new result as fact by the scientific community does not come easily. It requires repeated verification of the finding through independent, controlled experiments that are successive improvements on the original experiment through error analysis and better design, sometimes changing to entirely different principles of measurement. This sequence of experiments produces results that are expected to be more and more reliable. In the easy case, the fact fits in with established theory. In the difficult case when it does not, a change in paradigm might have to be contemplated. Under those circumstances, a much higher standard for the verification of the experimental results must be met.[2] I must say, however, that I would expect such circumstances to be rare in the policy context.

Many scientific facts, such as those dealing with the correctness of basic theories of physics and the values of physical constants, are of little interest in the policy domain. However, some questions of interest to government might be completely answered by a scientific fact.

Figure 1: Scientific Fact

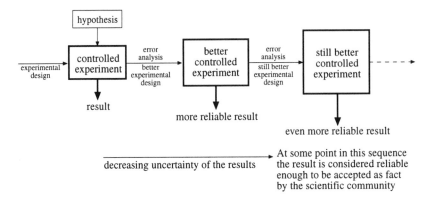

Here are some examples. Is a new fleece material for children's pyjamas a fire hazard according to a particular standard test for flammability? Does a new drug meet the criteria for approval set out in the Canada *Food and Drug Act* (Canada, 1995)? Is a particular species endangered? Does a given gasoline additive produce an airborne health hazard? When the policy question is narrowly defined, in a way that mirrors closely the reductionist approach of science, the scientific fact may be both necessary and sufficient for policy purposes. In my view, that circumstance is more likely to occur in the implementation of existing legislation and regulations than in the formation of new policy.

More generally, however, a scientific fact that is of interest to government is necessary but not sufficient for public policy purposes. For example, the fact that natural causes have from time to time produced significant episodes of climate warming is necessary in developing our understanding of climate change, but it would be just one of the many scientific facts that we need, together with other considerations that are described later, in order to develop good public policy in respect to meeting Canada's commitment to the Kyoto Accord.

There may be occasions, of course, when a new scientific fact is so compelling that it creates an imperative for new public policy. This would seem to occur when the scientific fact identifies a cause of some hazardous, perhaps unfamiliar, effect on people and their environment. The causal link between smoking and lung cancer is such a fact.[3]

SCIENTIFIC PREDICTION

It seems to me, however, that questions put to scientists in the context of public-policy formulation are much broader than the narrow questions already discussed. The goal is likely to be the solution of some pressing problem involving a large and complex social or natural system about which too little is known. The problem itself might be serious and urgent, but difficult to define precisely. Anecdotal evidence may far outweigh the scientific, and the problem may, in fact, be perceived to be one thing and turn out to be something else.

How do scientists offer advice in such circumstances? They make a prediction using a model of the system in question. The elements of that process are shown in Figure 2.

The model used for a scientific prediction begins with component models of the interacting processes that might be expected to be important in determining the behaviour of the whole system. The selection is made on the basis of experience, theory, or even intuition. The models of these phenomena are fitted into an appropriate mathematical structure that embodies techniques to convert input information into a prediction. There are two kinds of inputs: measurements and observations of a more qualitative sort. The model is tested against

Figure 2: Scientific Prediction

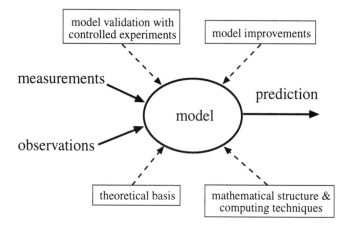

available measurements wherever possible, and is improved empirically to make the fit better. It also has to be validated, in full or component by component, whenever the opportunity arises to test it against a controlled experiment. Relevant theoretical developments lead to further improvements that increase its reliability. The process of improvement continues as observations accumulate, more measurements become possible, new relevant science facts come to light, new mathematical techniques are developed, computers get faster, etc.

The model of the atmosphere used to produce weather forecasts is probably the best developed model for scientific prediction. Its theoretical basis is well established, namely the Navier-Stokes equations of fluid mechanics. Its mathematical structure and techniques are a finite-difference grid that approximates the map of the region in question, and various computer programs for solving these equations numerically. The inputs are measurements that come from weather stations, complemented by observations from satellites. The output is the daily weather forecast. The model is being tested on a daily basis, and many people are continuously engaged in validating and improving it. For example, the component models of evaporation from the land, radiation from clouds, and atmospheric turbulence are changing as a result of research on those specific phenomena.

Today's weather model is the product of decades of research and refinement. It is vastly different from the tools available to the scientists who are asked to make a prediction of fish stocks and advise on the closing or opening up of a particular inshore fishery, say. The local problem depends on many factors, some of them local, some remote, some known, many more unknown, some that involve the behaviour of people who might be controlled by policy, and many others that depend on nature and are neither fully understood nor controllable. That complexity makes it unclear even what scientific disciplines should be involved in developing a model. But the questions that have to be answered in arriving at policy recommendations are very basic. When the catch in a particular bay declines sharply, does it mean that the fishery as a whole has declined, or that the fish have gone somewhere else? When the catch increases, does it mean that the fishery is recovering, or could it mean only that more of a declining fishery have come into this particular bay? People's livelihoods depend on the policy decisions that are based on the answers to such simple-sounding basic questions.

Under such circumstances, the scientists and government must have realistic expectations of one another and of themselves. Government cannot expect scientists to give advice with certainty and neither can it create the expectation among the public that it will solve the problem just as soon as the scientists get it right. Scientists, on the other hand, cannot expect their predictions to be treated as imperatives by decision-makers. They must recognize the limitations of their models, and acknowledge that there may be cases in which the pressure of time will not allow them to produce a reliable scientific prediction. In such circumstances, they should be ready to look for other kinds of information, such as historical knowledge, that might help deal with the problem.

THE PLACE OF SCIENTIFIC ADVICE IN POLICY-MAKING

My final remarks deal with the place of scientific advice, whether based on fact or prediction, in the process of making policy. These ideas are based mainly on personal observations over a period of eight years of service as Deputy Minister in the Government of Ontario, which included membership on two principal policy committees of Cabinet in which senior Civil Servants and Ministers worked together on policy initiatives. I have seen nothing since that experience that would cause me to change the basic structure of what follows.

The framework for my remarks is a proposed hierarchy of five questions that have to be addressed in policy-making. These are shown in Figure 3. From the bottom, they are the "know-what" issues; followed by "know how"; then "know who, where, when"; "know why"; and finally "know whether". Once the policy-making process is launched, this hierarchy represents the order in which questions are actually answered. It can also be thought of as a listing of the questions in order of difficulty.[4]

Figure 4 shows the association that I make between the questions in the hierarchy and the factors that enter into policy-making. Science is associated with questions of substance, the know-what issues. The know-how issues are associated with technology. Answers to the issues of who, where and when are a matter of experience; in the case of government that experience might be in delivering programs. The next level, the know-why issues, deals with motivation. And the final level, the know-whether, calls for judgement and decision-making.

Figure 3: Hierarchy of Policy-Making Questions

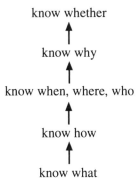

Figure 4: Relationship of Hierarchy Questions and Factors in
Policy-Making

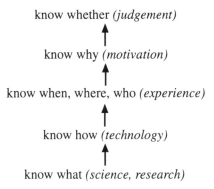

If the science is undisputed, then the answers to the know-what questions proceed to the next level of consideration. However, if there is a serious scientific dispute about substance, then the danger arises that one or other side of an unresolved issue might prematurely be taken as the scientific answer, for reasons that are not scientific. Worse yet, a scientific dispute might be used by individuals anywhere in the process as the reason for doing nothing. That temptation must be resisted, even if a scientifically sound solution cannot be found.

The know-why level, generally, is the level of entry into the policy-making process, as shown in Figure 5. A problem is brought to the attention of government, a campaign promise made, and the Civil Service is instructed to "look into it to see what might be done". The signal goes down from know why to know what, and the process starts at the bottom. Of course, policy is not usually made in one pass through the process. It is not at all unusual for the work to climb back up to the know-why level after many people have worked on it for a long time, only to be greeted with the question "Why are we thinking of doing this at all?" If the questioner is influential enough, that question can send the work right back down to the know-what level for another look, which may prove to be a very long look indeed.

Cabinet acts at the know-whether level. They decide whether to accept the policy recommendations that come up, in light of all the other considerations they must deal with. Figure 6 shows some of the considerations that intrude at that level. These are issues that do not come up through the policy-making process. They include, prominently, other interests, interests that were not included explicitly in the policy process. The name given to the considerations of such interests is "politics", by no means a pejorative.[5] The possibility of strategic issues and unintended consequences that had not been considered before arise here, as do issues of timing, external pressures, events, etc. Economic impacts of social policies and social impacts of economic policies, and environmental impacts of both, which might not have emerged earlier should come into consideration here. And, of course, there are

Figure 5: Level of Policy-Making

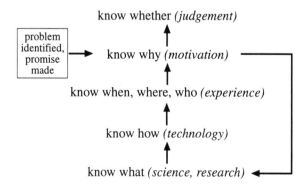

Figure 6: Policy at Cabinet Level

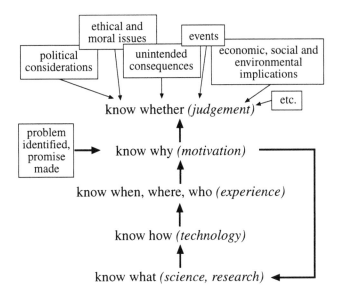

additional issues such as consistency with the values and philosophy of the governing party, obligations under international treaties, and possibly even with related but still unannounced intentions of the government.

Finally, we have to realize that there are two fundamental incompatibilities between the scientists at the know-how level and the decision-makers at the know-whether level (Figure 7). First, science is reductionist, but government decisions have to be holistic. Science divides problems into bite-size questions that can be answered, but governments have to try to optimize large interacting systems under various constraints.[6] The second incompatibility is related to certainty. Science cannot produce results with certainty. Even the scientific fact, discussed earlier, is always somewhat uncertain. Science advice in the policy-making process is much more uncertain, for reasons already discussed. Yet government decisions have to be binary. This proposal is approved; that one not. This will be done, and that not. This behaviour will be allowed; that behaviour not. You cannot make policies that direct something to be done "nineteen times out of twenty". However flexible and conditional a policy might be, it either exists or it does not.

Figure 7: Scientists and Decision-Makers

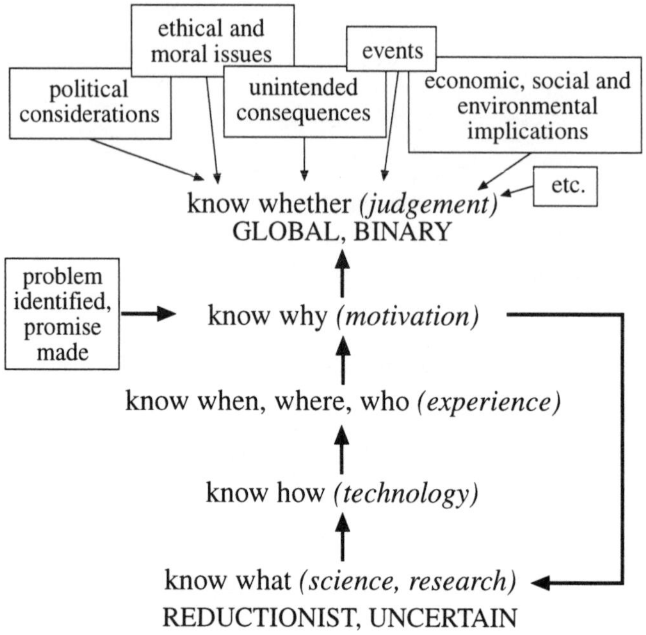

CONCLUSION

The conclusion from this is that science has a very important, indeed often essential, place in the policy-making process, but it rarely stands alone. Science generally does not produce policy imperatives or policy prescriptions, and scientists should recognize the importance of the other issues that must enter into consideration.

Likewise, decision-makers have to be ready to admit that they make judgements, and be ready to defend those judgements. The decision-makers must not claim that their decisions are dictated by science, and likewise they must resist any temptation to select those pieces of scientific advice that support the judgements they make for other reasons.

Perhaps no such understanding was needed in an earlier, simpler time. Scientists did science, decision-makers made policy, and it probably did not matter very much if they did not always work together all that well. But today, many of the issues that governments must cope with are driven by advances in science and technology, and the growing impact of human activity on nature requires a deep new understanding of many increasingly interrelated phenomena. In this new setting, I believe that the welfare of a nation requires that its scientists and its decision-makers in government must work in closer harmony than ever before in developing public policy.

NOTES

1. Department of Fisheries and Oceans and the Health Protection Branch of Health Canada.
2. At the time of writing, a dispute about this very process has become visible in the high-energy physics community. The subject is charge-parity violation, or the asymmetry between matter and anti-matter. The issue is whether a recent result obtained with high statistical certainty at Fermilab is the confirmation of a previous result obtained with much less statistical certainty at CERN (European Organization for Nuclear Research) in 1988, or an entirely new finding. The debate has spilled over into the general literature; see McDonald (1999).
3. As this paper was being edited for publication, new data appeared on the link between second-hand smoke and strokes. If and when that causal link becomes established as fact, various levels of government may introduce new or tighter policies on smoking in public places.
4. Another view is that this is also the order of responsibility and salary in the Public Service, and in many corporations as well. At the level of the individual, it can represent both growing maturity in the sense of developing the ability to understand and deal with such questions, and progress in a career.
5. It is ironic that in the heat of Question Period, Members of Parliament sometimes criticize each other's questions or answers as "politics".
6. Opposition politicians, likewise, enjoy the luxury of being able to focus their criticisms on one issue at a time. Politicians who find themselves in government with prior parliamentary experience only in Opposition have been known to admit that the necessary change of perspective is a shock.

REFERENCES

Canada (1995), "Food and Drug Act and Regulations", *New Drugs*, Sections C.08.001 to C.08.004, Ottawa: Supply and Services Canada.

McDonald, K.A. (1999), "Claim by Fermilab Physicists Sets Off Angry Dispute over Scientific Priority", *Chronicle of Higher Education* 45(27), p. A15.

CHAPTER 14

Canada's Policies and Investments in S&T: Where Do We Go from Here?

A.J. Carty

From a vantage point at the beginning of the twenty-first century, the Canadian scientific community will look back on the 1990s as a period of severe turbulence in the funding of research and development. It was a roller-coaster ride which saw the new (1993) Liberal government first undertake a comprehensive science and technology (S&T) review in 1994-95. From this review, much maligned at the time, emerged a document, *Science and Technology for the New Century* which laid out certain goals and operating principles for the years to the millennium. Unfortunately, any short-term positive impacts which the S&T review might have had were immediately overtaken by a maelstrom of budget cuts announced in the February 1995 budget as part of a massive Program Review designed to downsize government departments and agencies and reduce Canada's budgetary deficit. Science and technology were not immune to these cuts — reductions of 10 to 15 per cent for the Federal Granting Councils, 17 per cent for the National Research Council (NRC) and more than 30 per cent in some government departments represented a major set-back for research in Canada. However, in 1997 the tide began to turn. With the deficit under control, the Liberal government took the first steps in the 1997 budget to begin reinvesting in research, knowledge and innovation. Successive budgets in 1998 and 1999 continued the trend with new or enhanced investments in existing programs and a series of new initiatives focused on the research base and technology development ends of the research and development (R&D) spectrum. The 1999 budget alone announced $1.8 billion of new investment in science and technology.

Given this background it is of more than passing interest to look at global trends in R&D investments and to compare Canada's recent performance with that of other countries. How have we fared in comparison with our principal trading partners and competitors?

INTERNATIONAL TRENDS IN GERD-GDP RATIOS

In the 1960s, the Organization for Economic Co-operation and Development (OECD) developed an indicator — the gross expenditure on research and development (GERD), which, when normalized by dividing it by the gross domestic product (GDP), provided a measure of the intensity of R&D investment in that country. The GERD-GDP ratios allow a comparison of the relative R&D investments across countries. Because of its simplicity, the GERD-GDP ratio has been adopted widely not just as a measure of R&D performance, but also by implication, as an indicator, a bell-wether, so to speak, of technological advancement and industrial competitiveness.

The Canadian GERD-GDP ratio has been hovering around the 1.5 per cent mark for the last 30 years, except in the 1970s when it dropped below 1 per cent. That was the period when the Liberal government of the time under Pierre Trudeau was more interested in social issues (bilingualism, the Just Society, medicare) than in science. The distribution of wealth was more important than its creation according to the actions of the government at the time.

When OECD began GERD-GDP comparisons in the 1960s, Canada was well behind its competitors. The United States was above three — two times Canada's ratio. So the Science Council of Canada, later killed by the Mulroney government, proposed that Canada set a target of 2 per cent in the near term, up from 1.47 per cent at the time. By the mid-1990s the ratio was 1.55. This benchmark has been very difficult to budge and at one point, government policy-makers began to focus on the second decimal behind the decimal point!

But, let's take a more detailed look at the numbers.

A selection of GERD-GDP ratios for various countries is depicted in Figure 1 and a more detailed listing is reproduced in Table 1. Unfortunately, these ratios are not for the most recent year but they do illustrate several significant points:

- Only six countries — Sweden, Japan, South Korea, Switzerland, Finland and the United States — have values above 2.5. Korea is a recent arrival in this group of countries that invest heavily in R&D.
- Germany, Israel, France, the Netherlands, Denmark and the United Kingdom, all developed industrialized countries, are in a second group with GERD-GDP ratios of 1.90 to 2.5.
- Taiwan, like Korea, is an Asian Tiger and has risen rapidly to be close to two. Singapore is also rising. These countries have made a commitment to increase rapidly their R&D expenditures to try to compete with the leaders in the developed world.
- Canada at 1.6 is above only Italy in the list of G7 nations.

When trends in GERD-GDP ratios for the G7 countries over the last decade are examined (Figure 2) the following observations can be made:

- GERD-GDP ratios for most developed countries have been static (United States) or trending down (Japan, France, United Kingdom, Germany). Of the G7 countries, only Canada has shown a slight increase over the period 1991-98. Of course, it must be remembered that both the numerator and denominator in the GERD-GDP can change. A rapidly increasing GDP presents a challenge for increased R&D investment if the ratio is to stay constant. In other words, a very much larger absolute dollar investment in R&D may not effect an upward surge in GERD/GDP if GDP increases. In fact, over the past twenty years overall Canadian R&D investment has increased from approximately $2 billion to $13 billion (a factor of about 7x) even though the GERD-GDP ratio has not changed substantially (Figure 3).
- Although Figure 2 is not sufficiently up to date to reflect the most recent statistics, anecdotal information from heads of research agencies in the G7 countries suggests that for 1999-2000 the trend in government investment in R&D is up and cutbacks appear to be over. Governments in the United Kingdom, France and the United States as well as Canada are reinvesting in R&D.

When GERD-GDP ratios are broken down into their public/private sector components, some further interesting trends emerge (Figures 4 and 5). The most notable, and with the possible exception of Japan, the most consistent trend is that the percentages of GERD financed by government have declined substantially over the period 1990-97. For example, in the United States, the percentage of GDP financed by government has declined from 43 to 44 per cent of GERD in 1990 to 32 per cent in 1997. In Canada the decline has been less, from 34 per cent of GERD to 31 per cent.

Table 1

R&D EXPENDITURES

TOTAL EXPENDITURE ON R&D

1997

Percentage of GDP

ranking		%
1	SWEDEN	3.594 2
2	JAPAN	2.829 1
3	KOREA	2.791 1
4	SWITZERLAND	2.739 1
5	FINLAND	2.711
6	USA	2.546
7	GERMANY	2.401
8	ISRAEL	2.290
9	FRANCE	2.259
10	NETHERLANDS	2.089 1
11	DENMARK	1.937
12	TAIWAN	1.922
13	UNITED KINGDOM	1.900 1
14	SLOVENIA	1.695 2
15	AUSTRALIA	1.672 1
16	BELGIUM	1.585 2
17	NORWAY	1.558
18	CANADA	1.555
19	ICELAND	1.540
20	AUSTRIA	1.533
21	IRELAND	1.523 2
22	SINGAPORE	1.489
23	CZECH REPUBLIC	1.181
24	ITALY	1.054
25	NEW ZEALAND	0.981 2
26	RUSSIA	0.946
27	SPAIN	0.885
28	INDIA	0.770 1
29	POLAND	0.761 1
30	SOUTH AFRICA	0.746 1
31	HUNGARY	0.723
32	CHILE	0.645
33	CHINA	0.644
34	PORTUGAL	0.583 2
35	BRAZIL	0.568 2
36	GREECE	0.476 4
37	TURKEY	0.452 1
38	ARGENTINA	0.368 2
39	MEXICO	0.309 2
40	HONG KONG	0.288 2
41	PHILIPPINES	0.218 5
42	MALAYSIA	0.199
43	COLOMBIA	0.195 2
44	THAILAND	0.180
45	INDONESIA	0.092 2
46	VENEZUELA	0.006
	LUXEMBOURG	-

R&D EXPENDITURES

BUSINESS EXPENDITURE ON R&D

1997

US$ millions

ranking		US$ millions
1	USA	153,691
2	JAPAN	92,466 1
3	GERMANY	34,314
4	FRANCE	19,257
5	UNITED KINGDOM	14,533 1
6	KOREA	9,899 1
7	ITALY	6,582
8	SWEDEN	6,173 2
9	CANADA	6,166
10	SWITZERLAND	5,712 1
11	NETHERLANDS	4,368 1
12	TAIWAN	3,345
13	AUSTRALIA	3,229 1
14	RUSSIA	2,917
15	BELGIUM	2,782 1
16	CHINA	2,702
17	SPAIN	2,328
18	FINLAND	2,234
19	DENMARK	2,050
20	NORWAY	1,424 2
21	AUSTRIA	1,417 4
22	BRAZIL	1,308 2
23	ISRAEL	1,058
24	SINGAPORE	885
25	IRELAND	636 2
26	SOUTH AFRICA	485 1
27	POLAND	419 1
28	INDIA	378 1
29	CZECH REPUBLIC	352
30	GREECE	235 2
31	TURKEY	213 1
32	MEXICO	184 2
33	ARGENTINA	158 2
34	NEW ZEALAND	158 2
35	MALAYSIA	142
36	HUNGARY	137
37	COLOMBIA	132 2
38	PORTUGAL	121 2
39	INDONESIA	95 3
40	CHILE	77
41	THAILAND	42 2
42	ICELAND	41
43	HONG KONG	32 2
44	PHILIPPINES	3 4
	LUXEMBOURG	-
	SLOVENIA	-
	VENEZUELA	-

Source: *The World Competitiveness Yearbook 1999.*

Figure 1: Overall R&D Investment: 1997 GERD as a Percentage of GDP

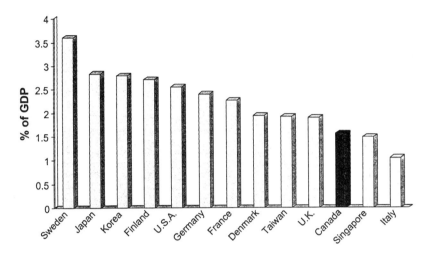

Source: *The World Competitiveness Yearbook 1999.*

Figure 2: GERD as a Percentage of GDP

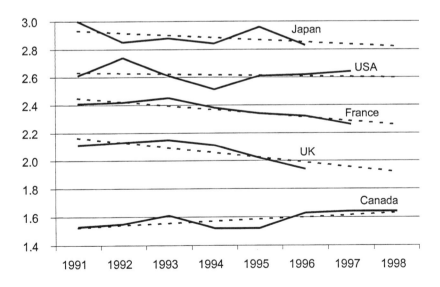

Note: Dashed lines are best least squares fits indicating overall trends.

Source: OECD, November 1998.

Figure 3: Canada: GERD by Major Sources of Funds, 1975-1997

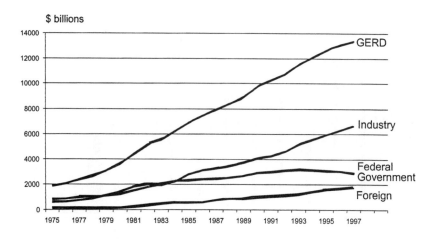

Figure 4: Percentage of GERD Financed by Government for
Selected G7 Countries

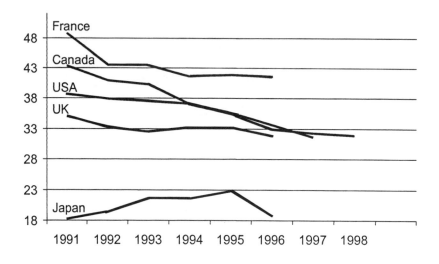

Source: OECD, November 1998.

Figure 5: Percentage of GERD Financed by Industry for Selected
G7 Countries

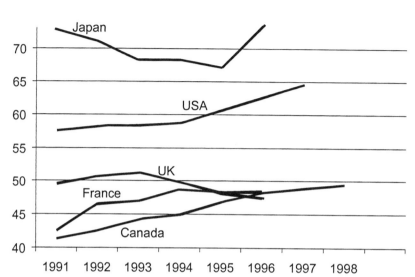

Source: OECD, November 1998.

In sharp contrast and perhaps again not well appreciated is the fact
that throughout the G7, with the possible exception of one country, the
United Kingdom, the percentage of GERD financed by industry has
increased significantly (Figure 5). For example, in France there has
been a growth in the percentage of GERD financed by industry to approximately 48 per cent (from 42 per cent in 1990). In Canada the
increase has been smaller than in the United States and France but
nevertheless has been from about 43 to 48 per cent.

CANADIAN TRENDS

In the case of Canada, there are some specific trends that are worth
pointing out, in part because they may not be generally appreciated.
Figure 6 illustrates the following points:

• Over the period 1988-98 private sector investment in R&D grew
steadily from about $3 billion to above $9 billion in 1998.

- Canadian government funding first rose modestly from just over $2 billion then plateaued and tailed off at just over $3 billion in 1998. This number will likely grow significantly in the 1999-2000 year as a result of announced new expenditures in the February 1999 budget.
- Foreign direct investment in R&D has more than doubled from under $1 billion per annum in 1988 to $2.5 billion in 1998.

A word of caution needs to be injected here in the interpretation of GERD-GDP statistics. Clearly GERD-GDP ratios will vary depending on what is included as expenditures on R&D. Not every country will have exactly the same definition of an R&D expenditure and indeed changes in interpretation may influence reported numbers. Furthermore, GERD-GDP ratios are at best only a very crude measure of a country's ability to innovate and R&D is only one component of innovation, albeit an important one. We need tools and measurements that are much more precise and inclusive than GERD-GDP to capture a country's innovation capacity. In other words, other elements of the innovation system must somehow be factored into the equation to

Figure 6: Canada: GERD by Funding Sector

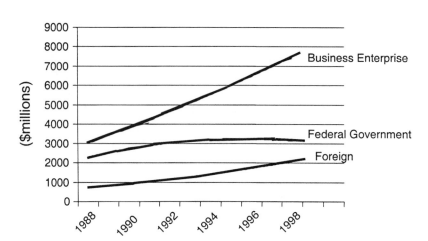

Note: All figures adjusted to 1992 constant dollars.

Source: Statistics Canada – Science Statistics, November 1998.

measure technological competitiveness. Michael Porter has said that "Innovation is the central issue in economic growth." But can we quantify it and understand more precisely how R&D investments impact upon it? There is a need for further insights here.

SUMMARY COMMENTS ON CANADA'S RECENT PERFORMANCE

From the particular viewpoint of Canada there have been several significant and promising recent developments. Over the last three federal budgets Canada has made considerable progress in reinvesting in R&D in Canada after massive budget cuts in 1995-96, 1996-97 and 1997-98.

This new commitment to a knowledge-based economy has benefited basic and targeted research in the universities through restoration of the funding levels of the Granting Councils at 1994-95 levels (prior to Program Review) and subsequent increases in budgets over these levels; networks and partnerships *via* the establishment of a firm base level of funds for the Networks of Centres of Excellence Program and incremental funding; investments in university infrastructure through the establishment of the $1 billion Canada Foundation for Innovation; creation of the Canadian Institutes for Health Research (CIHR), which represents a new vision for health research in Canada. When fully operational CIHR (which will incorporate the current Medical Research Council together with its funding) will have a steady state budget of $500 million per annum and will integrate all aspects of health research in the universities in Canada. There has also been increased funding for industrial R&D (increases to NRC's IRAP program and Technology Partnerships Canada) for both small companies or larger companies engaged in early stage, high-risk R&D and commercialization of technology. Also in February 1999, $55 million was made available to federal departments and agencies for R&D in biotechnology.

Details of this supplemental funding are captured in Table 2. What interpretation can one put on these observations and what are the likely impacts for Canada as it competes in the global economy?

From a uniquely Canadian perspective, the signs seem to be rather positive. Contrary to the overall downward trend in other countries over twenty years, total investment in R&D as seen by the GERD-GDP ratios is up. Industry is contributing more; see Figure 3. Our *total* expenditures on R&D are large compared to most of the world

Table 2: 1997-1999 Federal R&D Funding Decisions

| | (Incremental Funding in $million)* | | | | |
	1997-98	1998-99	1999-00	2000-01	2001-02
CFI*	800	200			
NSERC	71	25	25	25	
NCE	47	47	77	77	77
SSHRC	13	5	5	5	
NRC (Excluding IRAP)	16	5	5	5	
NRC/IRAP		26	34	34	34
Biotechnology			15	20	20
TPC ($250 million funding in 1996-97)	50	50	50	50	50
MRC		40	28	28	28
CIHR				65	175
Canadian Space Agency**	120	41	152	237	
Smart Communities			15	30	15
GeoConnections		12	12	12	

Notes: * Approved funding not necessarily spent in the current year.
(For CFI case, funds spread over five years).
** Restoration of agency base.

and recently have been increasing. The Government of Canada has, *via* recent budget decisions and statements of the Minister of Finance, committed to a knowledge-based economy in which R&D and innovation play key roles. Indeed the words and phrases "knowledge-based economy" and "innovation" have become embedded in political jargon. There is no doubt that continuity of government commitment and investment in R&D in Canada over three federal budgets has turned the tide and brought a new sense of optimism to the research community. However, these very positive changes should not obscure fundamental underlying weaknesses in the structure of Canadian industry.

For example, the transition of the Canadian economy to a knowledge-based one is severely hindered by the peculiar structure of our industry. Of the top ten companies in Canada (Table 3) in terms of earnings only one, Nortel Networks, invests heavily in R&D (Nortel spends in excess of US$2 billion on R&D annually). The three largest manufacturing companies in Canada, General Motors of Canada Ltd., Ford Motor Co. of Canada Ltd. and Chrysler Canada Ltd., are not listed among the top investors in R&D nor are the natural resources companies which have played such a large role in the "old" Canadian economy of the past.

The listing of top R&D spenders in Canada (Table 3) includes Nortel, Pratt & Whitney Canada Inc., Merck Frosst Canada Inc., IBM Canada Ltd., Ericsson Communications Inc., Newbridge Networks Corp. and Bombardier. As well, the federal agencies NRC and NSERC each spend approximately $500 million annually on R&D. All of the top R&D spending companies depend heavily on knowledge and innovation for their competitiveness and survival. These are the new economy companies of the twenty-first century in the knowledge-based sectors of information and telecommunications, pharmaceuticals and biotechnology and aerospace.

However, the fact that no Canadian company other than Nortel spends more than NRC and NSERC on R&D points to a structural failure in our industry: too few of our large companies invest heavily in research and innovation. We have a major gap in Canada, largely in the middle

Table 3:   Top Ten Canadian Revenue and R&D Firms

Top Ten Revenue	*($billion)*	*Top Ten R&D*	*($million)*
1. BCE Inc.	33.7	1. Northern Telecom	3,100
2. Northern Telecom	15.7	2. PWC	420
3. Seagram Company	12.9	3. Merck Frosst	265
4. Royal Bank of Canada	17.6	4. IBM Can.	224
5. Cdn Imp Bank of Commerce	16.7	5. Newbridge	186
6. Bank of Montreal	14.5	6. AECL	167
7. TransCanada PipeLines	14.3	7. Ericsson Com.	160
8. George Weston Ltd.	13.9	8. Magna Interna.	138
9. Bank of Nova Scotia	13.2	9. Bombardier	131
10. Thomson Corporation	8.8	10. Corel	124
		NRC	**507**
		NSERC	**539**

part of the R&D spectrum, which in other countries is filled by medium to long-term R&D in corporate, industrial R&D labs. This market "failure" virtually demands that the gap be filled, for the forseeable future by public sector investment — particularly in strategic R&D carried out in wealth-generating areas by government labs, Centres of Excellence and industry-university partnerships. Indeed I would argue that there is a very specific and particular need in Canada, perhaps unique to this country, to invest in R&D at the interface between basic research and industrial development simply to bridge the gap and lever greater industrial investment.

In 1995-96, the S&T Review outlined a series of principles and objectives for science and technology in Canada. These are brought together in Figure 7. Without commenting in detail on the success or failure of each of these objectives it is becoming increasingly clear that overall Canada has made substantial progress toward the overall goals set forth in this document. With a continued government commitment to R&D and innovation, the future looks brighter than it has for many years.

Figure 7: "Science and Technology for the New Century"
1996 S&T Strategy

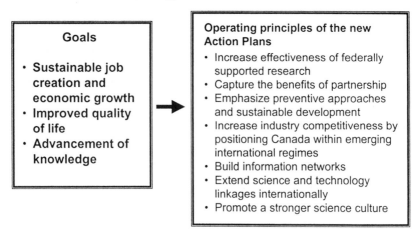

Goals

- **Sustainable job creation and economic growth**
- **Improved quality of life**
- **Advancement of knowledge**

Operating principles of the new Action Plans

- Increase effectiveness of federally supported research
- Capture the benefits of partnership
- Emphasize preventive approaches and sustainable development
- Increase industry competitiveness by positioning Canada within emerging international regimes
- Build information networks
- Extend science and technology linkages internationally
- Promote a stronger science culture

CHAPTER 15

Science as Part of Public Policy

P. Milliken

My emphasis here is on science and science policy as part of public policy. At this conference in 1996, I urged scientists to contact politicians to discuss their work, explain the value of their work and even show them how it is being done. I said how important it was to convince people in public life that science was important. I know that this message has been taken seriously and I have lots of evidence to show that this is the case. I get regular invitations to tour labs and I know that many of my colleagues do too.

The government has been made aware of the need for more scientific research monies through an extensive letter-writing campaign. This campaign, along with concerted lobby activities, is making a difference. Visits from organized science-based lobby groups have become commonplace. During the annual Social Sciences and Humanities Research Council (SSHRC) lobby day on Parliament Hill members of SSHRC gather and pay visits to their Members of Parliament to urge them to support funding for the SSHRC. The researchers review the importance to them of the grants they receive as well as the employment it generates by providing the ability to hire students and others. Other groups also visit: the Canadian Association of University Teachers and the Royal Society of Canada, for example. These meetings have created an atmosphere or situation in which Members of Parliament feel more comfortable talking about science policy, supporting science policy and discussing the importance of science in our daily lives. Many of them have come to realize that these scientists are responsible, in a very direct way, for some of the tangible benefits that they see daily and for giving them answers to many of the issues with which Members of Parliament must deal. Another very successful venture has been a regular meeting of the "Bacon and Eggheads Breakfasts" in Ottawa. This is a meeting of scientists and Members of Parliament for the purpose of sharing information.

Policy changes that have resulted are a reflection of this lobbying, along with the significant changes that have taken place in public discourse in Canada over the last three or four years. In almost every speech the Industry Minister makes, the terms "knowledge-based economy" or "global economy" appear regularly. The Finance Minister particularly is keen on the latter, but he talks about the other as well. We live in a knowledge-based economy, and therefore training is becoming more important, scientific advances are more rapid and having individuals learn about these advances and the latest technology and techniques has become more important than it ever was. Peter Drucker said:

> The knowledge society will inevitably become far more competitive than any society we have yet known for the simple reason that with universal accessibility to knowledge there will be no excuses for non-performance and the same will be true for companies, industries and organizations of all kinds. It will be true for individuals too.
>
> Knowledge after all is not like other factors of production, such as land or even financial capital. There is no physical limit to it. The creation or consumption of it in one place does not limit the ability of others to create or consume it. If we both have information, we both can gain in personal and economic terms if we share it with one another. Knowledge resources are not limited by boundaries or nation states. They are limited only by our ability to innovate and our ability to connect. (January 1998).

The whole idea of the exchange of information and connections in order to share knowledge has become something widely accepted, not just by Ministers, but by Members of Parliament and by the public. This change has meant that it has been relatively easy for the Minister of Finance to change funding arrangements.

There have been big increases in spending for science at the National Research Council of Canada (NRC), the Canadian Institutes for Health Research (CHIR), the Centres of Excellence, the Canada Foundation for Innovation and the Millennium Scholarship Fund. All these reflect an awareness in government of the importance of science, education and knowledge. While there has been criticism for lack of spending in other places, these particular areas have been supported.

But there has been another change as well and that is, I think, a change on the part of Members of Parliament who previously criticized expenditures on science. The Canadian Taxpayers Foundation published a list of what they considered useless grants for science and research, particularly in the social sciences area, although they included some from science. They questioned the value of some research projects and these lists were published monthly in a newsletter. Grants were attacked as a waste of taxpayers' dollars. You do not hear of these attacks much from the Canadian Taxpayers Foundation any more in that particular area and you certainly do not hear them very much any more from the Opposition in the House of Commons. For some years, the Reform Party, in particular, would criticize these expenditures. When criticisms are raised, they receive less media coverage than before. In other words, the media does not find it attractive any longer to attack scientists. Reporters are relying on scientists for opinions. They are looking to experts to back up some of the stories they want to publish.

We are being faced with more issues that require scientific knowledge. For example, some people are very concerned about the regulation of herbal remedies. If such remedies were placed within the restrictions of the *Food and Drug Act*, costs might increase or they might no longer be available. Advice from scientists in the Department of Health has obviously been very important in this area.

The second issue involves the availability of new drugs. Canada has been slow in some cases in permitting the use of certain drugs. A drug that enhances milk production in cows, recently disallowed by the Department of Health, was the subject of many letters from people who were concerned that this drug would filter through to humans and impair their health.

The public is also concerned about the growing role of the Internet and the lack of any legislation leading to restrictions on its use.

These are all issues that concern Canadians and lead them to write to the members of Parliament of all parties. All require some scientific information, and in every case, Members of Parliament have been helped by the scientific community in dealing with concerns. There is more and more inclusion of the scientific community in government decision-making.

What of the future? My message is, do not stop doing whatever you have been doing, both in your scientific work and more importantly in your public relations work. Scientists need to communicate that their work: (a) is taking place, (b) is important and (c) could affect people's well-being. Scientists were working without talking about their work and the messages were not available. This is changing now, in part because the media is interested in promoting it, but also because people who are doing this work are talking to the public about it and explaining it, even in the modest ways I have described and in the one-to-one meetings. I think these are very important.

Someone at the Bacon and Eggheads Breakfast asked me, "How can we increase attendance here?" That is easy. Ask all the scientists to invite a Member of Parliament. Most members are free at breakfast and most would appreciate the opportunity to visit. Contact is important and information can be passed on to others. Members take a lot of pride in the events that are happening with their constituents or with people they know. Learning about the important scientific discoveries or research being done is one of those pleasures and is something that Members are pleased to be able to discuss.

The message throughout all this has been the importance of education, re-education and continuing education. Education of politicians is a significant part of a scientist's work. Ultimately, if politicians are going to make decisions as to funding, and these are important, it is imperative that politicians be cognizant of the effects of the decisions they are making.

CHAPTER 16

James Bond, Science and Policy-Making

C.E.S. Franks

> Largo, "Are you as good a loser as you are a winner, Mr. Bond?"
> James Bond, "I don't know. I've never lost" (*Never Say Never Again,* I. Fleming).

> "Bond's mind was clear again ... now the cards were waiting for him in the shoe.... They must not fail him. He felt his heart lift at the prospect of what was to come" (*Casino Royale,* I. Fleming).

I have always liked this fantastic notion of the super-hero exercising his macho powers to will the cards to do what he wants. Bond not only defeats human adversaries, he also makes cards defy the laws of statistics and bend to his demands. He makes his own future against the impersonal forces of nature, as well as more credible human villains. For real heroes, like Hillary on Everest and Powell in the Grand Canyon, nature is a neutral obstacle, a series of forces and challenges to be defeated by skill, determination and strength. Bond's nature in the casino is the law of probability which neither determination nor strength help to defeat. Of course, most people who gamble in casinos and the like are motivated by feelings like Bond's, that they can, through pluck, determination and will alter immutable and impersonal odds in their favour.

This common human tendency, the belief that will, strength and virtue can beat the odds, affects government policy-making at least as much as it does investing in the stock market, buying lottery tickets and bidding at auctions. This paper looks at one example of this sort of wishful thinking masquerading as objective analysis in a crucial decision in British energy policy. It comes from 1959, when C.P. Snow was making his case about the two cultures; and it is a policy he may have had in mind as he wrote. It had important and far-reaching consequences for the economy and politics of Britain; and scientists were heavily involved in the studies and analyses that preceded it. It proved to be misguided; and was taken for the wrong reasons. We are now far enough distanced from it that we can see how and why the errors in analysis occurred.

In 1955, Britain undertook the world's first peaceful nuclear power programme. This decision came at that desperate postwar time when Britain had few successes, was losing her empire, was suffering from chronic energy shortages, especially of coal, and was looking for some way to reassert the industrial and technological superiority that had made her one of the great powers of the world. The decision to build Calder Hall, the world's first large-scale prototype of a peaceful nuclear power station, was taken in 1953. In 1955, the government announced, in the white paper, *A Programme of Nuclear Power* (United Kingdom, 1955), that it intended to build a series of magnox nuclear power stations based on the Calder Hall design of gas-cooled graphite-moderated reactors. This already ambitious plan was trebled at the time of the Suez crisis in 1957, with a new intention to build up to 6,000 megawatts of nuclear generating capacity.

Much of the impetus for the programme came from the scientists in Britain's atomic energy project. Sir Stanley Brown, later Chairman of the Central Electricity Generating Board, recalled that the first contact of the electricity supply industry with nuclear power came at a discussion at Harwell in 1950, where Sir John Cockcroft "sat like a benign sphinx listening to violently conflicting argument, and summing up that there seemed to be every possibility that uranium power would be no more costly than coal power" (Brown, 1969). Sir Christopher Hinton, who had led the engineering team for Calder Hall, suggested in 1953 that a series of reactors based on Calder Hall could be built for civilian purposes. A reworking of this proposal by an interdepartmental committee chaired by Burke Trend of Treasury became the white paper.

This development of peaceful nuclear power, along with its military twin brother, was the largest scientific and technological project ever undertaken in Britain. It consumed a vast proportion of Britain's scientific resources, and an even larger proportion of research funds. The scale of construction was large enough to make resources scarce for other scientific and industrial projects in Britain.

These nuclear-power decisions were based on a heady mixture of hard science, strategic assumptions and calculations, and beliefs that bordered on wishful thinking, if not magic. Some assumptions were a mixture of all three, such as "our civilization is based on energy" (United Kingdom, 1955). Reginald Maudling told the House of Commons that the "lesson to be drawn [from the nuclear power programme] is that in our energy policy our outlook must be bold and one in which we are prepared to take risks" (House of Commons *Debates*, April 30, 1957, p. 566:35). Prime Minister Macmillan described the thinking of the Conservative government of the time: "They talk a lot about the glories of the old Elizabethan Age, but they forget that that was a time when Britain was politically very insecure, between much greater empires. We only kept the country going then by taking tremendous risks and adventures. It's more like that today — it's exciting living on the edge of bankruptcy" (quoted in Sampson 1967, p 170). The James Bond mentality was hard at work.

In the event, every major social and economic assumption and prediction underlying the first nuclear-power programme proved to be wrong. Britain soon faced a glut of coal. Oil became plentiful and cheap. Nuclear power proved to be more expensive than predicted. No export markets emerged for British reactors. The reactors took longer to build, and were more costly, than had been estimated, as was the electricity they generated. Nuclear technology and science produced no significant spillover effects that helped other British industries. One factor ignored by both scientists and the politicians was that over half the cost of using electricity is in the distribution system and the means of consuming it. The Magnox reactors became a technological dead end, and produced no economic or industrial benefits. Nevertheless, the reactors embodied good science and engineering, and reliably and safely produced electricity. Unlike Chernobyl, they were not a technological and environmental disaster.

The arguments for the programme were based on predictions of long-term factors that were inherently uncertain. The programme demanded massive present-day investments, and diversion of scarce resources on the basis of these risky predictions of what a distant future would be like. Decision-makers not only failed to appreciate and take into account the risk and uncertainty associated with predictions, but consistently overestimated benefits and underestimated risks. The decisions were taken by a restricted set of individuals in an atmosphere of secrecy, and the mind-set of the times did not allow for questioning or scepticism about these assumptions and predictions. Scientists were as guilty of unreasonable optimism as politicians and administrators on both scientific and other factors. The policy illustrates the Bond mentality in accepting as facts highly uncertain and risky predictions. Britain's unhappy experience with nuclear power presaged that of the world. It has always been bedeviled by unreasonable and exaggerated hopes and fears.

Science in policy-making is a vastly different matter from policy for science. Policy-making is the most multi-disciplinary of activities, drawing, as it did on nuclear power, on the knowledge and analytical skills of scientists and engineers, the forecasts and analysis of economists, the abilities of industrialists and public servants and the beliefs and concerns of politicians, among many others. In this sort of decision-making no single participant can know all that there is to know. Each participant is essentially ignorant about some of the key factors and must rely on the knowledge and expert advice of others. Widely differing attitudes, experience and backgrounds, professional skills and knowledge bases have to be welded together to make a coherent programme. To the extent that individual decision-makers in nuclear energy had to trust and accept on faith the advice given by others, the decisions had an element of magic, of acceptance on the basis of belief and faith rather than knowledge. Nuclear power was treated as magic by politicians and scientists alike, and by the credulous press and public as well. Extraordinary things were expected of what was, in effect, only another, and a not very efficient, way of boiling water. Even if the cost of energy from the atom had been less than that of alternative energy sources, it would have had little economic effect.

C.P. Snow did not discuss the social sciences. Yet the real weaknesses in the atomic energy decisions were not in the science and engineering, which were outstanding, or in the capacity of the government and industry to administer the programme, which was far better than has been appreciated, but in the social science sphere: in the economic analysis, in the understanding of the place of energy in the economy, in a failure to identify the key components of industrial development, in a misperception of the role of energy in the economy, and particularly in the failure to recognize and come to terms with the risks and uncertainties in predictions and assumptions.

These human failings still bedevil policy-making in nuclear energy. Many studies have found nuclear energy to be among the least hazardous and most environmentally friendly of energy sources, but public and political perceptions are so negative that nuclear power is on the decline in most countries. At the same time, strict regulation imposes severe costs on nuclear energy, so much so that the cost per life saved (or other human measure) in nuclear energy is far greater than in most other energy sources, and in other major industrial activities such as manufacturing, mining, agriculture and transportation. This is not to defend nuclear energy, but to emphasize that perceptions of risk and uncertainty by the public and by decision-makers are often vastly at odds with these risks as calculated by knowledgeable experts. The James Bond syndrome, and other normal human ways of handling risk and uncertainty, can be severely dysfunctional in integrating science into public policy.

REFERENCES

Brown, S. (1969), "Cockcroft Memorial Lecture: The Background to the Nuclear Power Programmes", unpublished speech.

Sampson, A. (1967), *Macmillan: A Study in Ambiguity*, London: Penguin Books.

United Kingdom (1955), *A Programme of Nuclear Power*. Cmd. 9389, London: Her Majesty's Stationery Office.

PART VI

THE CULTURES OF
ACCOUNTABILITY

CHAPTER 17

Measuring the Commercialization of Intellectual Property by Universities: An Indicator of Accountability?

F.D. Gault

INTRODUCTION

Accountability reflects the values of society and that society is chang-ing. There is less hierarchy, more networks, more lobby groups for the environment, human rights and responsive governments, and a sense that, in the information society, there should be immediate answers to questions raised by the consumer, the voter or the lobby groups. This introduces tensions between those who manage resources and those who hold them accountable and this has implications for measure-ment, as well as management. This paper looks at one example of statistical measurement leading to indicators of the commercialization of intellectual property by universities in Canada, and argues that this measurement, and its use, are signs of change in the culture of accountability.

In developing the argument, new measurements of commercializa-tion of intellectual property are presented, along with a selection of the recommendations of the Expert Panel on the Commercialization of University Research to the Government of Canada. The new mea-sures and the recommendations are set into the context of the Cana-dian science and technology (S&T) system and the programme of sta-tistical measurement that is being developed to describe it.

A CHANGE IN CULTURE?

Accountability is not new. Wherever resources are allocated there are mechanisms to report to the community of interest on the disposition of those resources and there are people or institutions charged with ensuring that the reporting meets agreed standards. In the case of the federal government in Canada, Parliament allocates money by vote, Ministers report to Parliament on the disposition of funds and the Auditor General monitors process. This process is designed to ensure that resources are spent on the objectives for which they are granted and that they are allocated in such a way as to be effective in achieving the objectives and efficient in their use.

The measurements associated with this kind of accountability have, in the recent past, been input measures. In the case of research and development (R&D), Statistics Canada has, for forty years, collected and published the government expenditure on R&D and the number of full-time equivalent people engaged in the activity. Successive governments have monitored carefully the public expenditure on domestic R&D and compared it with the expenditure of the private sector. The gross domestic expenditure on research and development (GERD), expressed as a percentage of the gross domestic product (GDP) was used as a measure of the investment of the country in the generation of new knowledge and this was compared with the same ratio for other countries.

While this may seem limited, it was based on the so-called "linear model" in which research gave rise to development that generated inventions, some of which were commercialized (innovation) and then diffused through the economy, increasing welfare as a result. With such a model, the only policy question was whether to invest in research or not, and if so, whether to target particular fields or industries. The dominance of the GERD-GDP ratio as the indicator for international comparisons led to proposals for the setting of targets for increasing the ratio: an indicator of input-focused policy and accountability on input.

In this context, the audit and accountability process was expected to verify that the policy objective was achieved and in an effective manner with efficient use of resources. There is still a place for this kind of accountability, but it does not address the question of outputs of the activity and their longer term social and economic impact.

It was such a question in 1994 which gave rise to the review of science and technology activities of the federal government (Industry Canada, 1996). Reduced to its most basic form the question was: What does the government get for more than five billion dollars spent on S&T? The S&T review has been reported on elsewhere (Gault, 1998; Meisel, 1998), but it is introduced here to signal a change in focus on accountability from "What do you pay?" to "What do you get?".

RESPONDING TO CHANGE

Measurement

As part of the response to the question of outcomes, the Information System for Science and Technology Project was established at Statistics Canada in March 1996. The project itself was a concrete outcome of the S&T review and its purpose was to develop useful indicators of activity and a framework to tie them together into a coherent picture of science and technology. With the three years for which it had its initial funding, the project did develop a framework (Statistics Canada, 1999*b*) and a strategy for the next years of development (Statistics Canada, 1999*a*) for which funding has since been secured. The framework takes a systems approach and ties together information on the activities of actors in the system, their linkages and the outcomes of the activities that spanned knowledge generation, transmission and use. Examples of the activities are R&D, invention, innovation (commercial use of invention) and human-resource development related to all of these activities. Linkage measures are essential to understanding how the system works and some examples are measures of alliances among R&D performers, co-authorship of academic papers, and the commercialization of intellectual property held in universities and in government laboratories.

Information on the commercialization of intellectual property (IP) has long been a matter of interest to the Association of Universities and Colleges of Canada and an alliance was struck with Statistics Canada to develop a survey of intellectual property commercialization in collaboration with universities themselves. The ease with which this collaboration came together reflected a willingness to demonstrate, at an aggregate level, that Canadian universities did contribute to the economy and social welfare, while at the same time fulfilling their three basic functions of research, teaching and community service.

The result of the collaboration was the first such comprehensive and collaborative survey in Canada (Bordt and Read, 1999), followed by an improved second survey in 1999. The first survey looked at IP management policies, at barriers to commercialization, and at the licensing of IP and the spin-off companies created. This was in keeping with the interest in linkage measures and indicators of the flow of knowledge from the universities to the private sector.

Policy Advice

Another outcome of the S&T review was the creation of the Prime Minister's Advisory Committee on Science and Technology (ACST). It is chaired by the Minister of Industry, reports to the Cabinet Committee on Economic Union (CCEU) and provides advice on all matters relating to S&T. One of the initiatives of the ACST was to establish the Expert Panel on the Commercialization of University Research in October of 1998. The Panel produced its final report in May of 1999 (Advisory Committee on Science and Technology, 1999) and the recommendations of the Panel, if adopted by the government, will add to the ways in which universities are held accountable for the use of public funds.

The Panel drew extensively on the results of the first survey and provided an example of statistical measurement contributing to the policy process. Part of what the Panel learned was that about 62 per cent of the universities surveyed managed their intellectual property centrally and, during the previous five years, 43 per cent had filed patent applications. About one-third had licensed their technologies and there was also information on spin-off companies and the equity in them held by universities. While these results were on aspects of commercialization, the Panel had available to it other economic and social statistics to provide a context.

The focus of the report of the Panel was on how to maximize the returns to Canada from the commercialization of publicly funded research, a focus which led to the first of six recommendations:

> The federal government should require an explicit commitment from all recipients of federal research funding that they will obtain the greatest possible benefit to Canada, whenever the results of their federally funded research are used for commercial gain (Advisory Committee on Science and Technology, 1999).

This raises questions about what is meant by "benefit" and the report states that "the best way to measure Canada's commercialization performance is to examine rates of return on investment" and then to compare the results with those for American universities, while noting that there are both measurement and conceptual problems associated with this course of action. As a result, the Social Science and Humanities Research Council is encouraged to support additional research in this area and Statistics Canada is urged to consider implementing the recommendations in Annex 4 of the report.

Annex 4, "National Data Collection Requirements", offers six recommendations to Statistics Canada of which four were implemented in the second cycle of the survey, a case of the policy debate influencing the statistical process. The four recommendations, which were implemented, addressed coverage and content. The coverage was to include all Canadian universities and degree-granting colleges that secured public research grants, and research hospitals were to be added. The content was to be extended to include new questions proposed by the Panel on legal costs of commercialization and on frequency, magnitude and causes of benefits leaked to other countries.

Two recommendations were not implemented. One dealt with the rate of return on investments in university research and Canada-U.S. comparisons, which requires further research. The other urged the publication of university-specific responses, which raised the question of confidentiality under the Canadian *Statistics Act.*

The Chief Statistician of Canada may, by order, authorize the disclosure of "information relating to a person or organization in respect of which disclosure is consented to in writing by the person or organization concerned" (*Statistics Act*, 1985, section 17. (2) b). While Statistics Canada could seek such consent, refusal to disclose by some institutions would make it difficult to publish both university-specific results for some universities, as well as aggregate figures, without increasing the risk of residual disclosure. As the survey is voluntary, universities might well choose not to respond and this would affect the quality of the aggregate data.

There are some data on individual universities published by the Association of University Technology Managers. The Association has conducted an annual survey of university licensing since 1991 and in 1997 it reported on one hundred and thirty-two American and fourteen Canadian universities (Association of University Technology Managers,

1998). While the fourteen Canadian universities accounted for about half of all Canadian university-sponsored research, the fourteen institutions were the larger ones with a history of commercialization. As a consequence, the results were not representative of Canadian practice and the content of the survey was not as comprehensive as that conducted by Statistics Canada for the same period.

INDICATORS AND ACCOUNTABILITY

These two initiatives, the Statistics Canada project looking for indicators of knowledge flow to industry, as part of understanding the S&T system, and the Advisory Committee on Science and Technology Panel seeking specific measures of commercialization to support policy proposals, have resulted in an annual survey with the potential to satisfy both statistical and policy needs. Both objectives fit well with a growing interest in understanding network systems (de la Mothe, 1999), and in developing results-based evaluation.

Once there is a set of indicators on the commercialization of intellectual property, the stage is set for results-based performance assessment. This could include accounting to the federal government for the use of federal research funding and to the community in which the university is located for the use of funds from the provincial government. The results would include the creation of jobs through licensing of intellectual property and spin-off companies as well as other benefits of commercialization. The inputs would include federal research funding, provincial funding, and other sources.

However, just as the use of the GERD-GDP ratio biased the policy debate for decades, there is a danger of using misleading results-based performance measures as a basis for public accountability. As an example, consider the ratio of revenue from the licensing of intellectual property to the input of federal research funding as such an indicator. It could be misleading for several reasons. There is a time lag between the doing of the research and the invention that is protected by a patent, which can then be licensed for use by a firm in return for revenue. This would not matter if the university were stable over a number of years, however, the structure of activities in the university would almost certainly be different from that of other universities which might do comparatively more teaching, or community service, than research. The difference in structure would have to be taken into account before meaningful comparisons could be made and, for international comparisons, so also would differences in legal frameworks. Finally, the university might hire an academic who had done years of basic research at another institution and was on the verge of producing a number of valuable patents. How should this be counted?

The lesson from all of this is that no indicator should be used in isolation for policy or for accountability. A number of indicators should be used if meaningful comparisons are to be made and, in the case of commercialization, there is no shortage of possible indicators (The Impact Group, 1997). Indicators that link inputs with outputs require considerable analytical thought as there may be time lags and other reasons why the inputs are not closely linked with the outputs. This might require an analytical model of the inputs, the outputs, and the processes of transformation of the one into the other. And that is before there is an estimation of the social and economic impacts of the outputs over time.

CONCLUSIONS

The review of federal science and technology activities in 1994-96 contributed to a shift from input measures to linkage and output measures, and to a policy interest in results-based evaluation and accountability. The measurement of commercialization, with the co-operation of the universities is an indication that a change has taken place from a preoccupation with input measures to the use of outcome measures to demonstrate that the universities, in total, are contributing substantially to the creation of jobs and social welfare as a result of transferring their intellectual property to the market place. Commercialization measures can be used for accountability.

While the culture has shifted, care should be taken when using a small number of indicators to draw meaningful conclusions, or to make comparisons between universities or even between similar universities in different countries, or economies. This does not mean that indicators should not be developed and they are of use to individual institutions for comparing themselves with aggregates for similar universities. However, the development of indicators requires a systems approach in which indicators of activities, linkages and outcomes are tied together and are presented in an economic and social context. For the learning to be maximized, the work on building the indicators must continue to be shared in an undertaking of collaboration, such as the one fostered by Statistics Canada, supported by the Association of

Universities and Colleges in Canada, and contributed to by people from eighty-one Canadian universities.

NOTE

All of the working papers, research papers, survey questionnaires and reporting guides used in the Information System for Science and Technology Project are available at (http://www.statcan.ca/english/research/scilist.htm).

REFERENCES

Advisory Committee on Science and Technology (1999), "Public Investments in University Research: Reaping the Benefits", *Report of the Expert Panel on the Commercialization of University Research*, Ottawa: Industry Canada. (http://acst-ccst.gc.ca)

Association of University Technology Managers (1998), *Association of University Technology Managers Licensing Survey: Fiscal Year 1997*, Norwalk: AUTM.

Bordt, M. and Read, C. (1999), *Survey of Intellectual Property Commercialization in the Higher Education Sector, 1998*, 88F0006XPB No. 01, Ottawa: Statistics Canada. (http://www.statcan.ca/english/research/88F0006XIB/99001.pdf)

de la Mothe, J. (1999), "Empowering Information and Networks through Adaptive Public Policies", in *Information, Innovation and Impacts*, ed. J. de la Mothe and G. Paquet, Boston: Kluwer, pp. 273-289.

Gault, F.D. (1998), "The Federal Strategy for Science and Technology in Canada and Statistical Measurement", in *Statistics, Science and Public Policy*, ed. A.M. Herzberg and I. Krupka, Kingston: Queen's University, pp. 181-188.

The Impact Group (1997), *Commercialization of Intellectual Property in the Higher Education Sector: A Feasibility Study*, 88F0006XPB No. 11, Ottawa: Statistics Canada. (http://www.statcan.ca/english/research/88F0006XIB/97011.pdf)

Industry Canada (1996), *Science and Technology for the New Century: A Federal Strategy*, Ottawa: Supply and Services Canada.

Meisel, J. (1998), "Caesar and the Savants: Some Socio-Political Contexts of Science and Technology in Canada", in *Statistics, Science and Public*

Policy, ed. A.M. Herzberg and I. Krupka, Kingston: Queen's University, pp. 153-177.

Statistics Act, Revised Statutes of Canada, 1985, c. S19.

Statistics Canada (1999*a*), *A Five-Year Strategic Plan for the Development of an Information System for Science and Technology 1998*, Cat. No. 88-523-XPB, Ottawa: Statistics Canada. (http://www.statcan.ca/english/IPS/Data/88-523-XIE.htm)

_____ (1999*b*), *Science and Technology Activities and Impacts: A Framework for a Statistical Information System 1998*, Ca. No. 88-522-XPB, Ottawa: Statistics Canada. (http://www.statcan.ca/english/IPS/Data/88-522-XIE.htm)

CHAPTER 18

Medicare and Canadian Federalism

L. Horlick

Medicare is considered to be the most valued social programme in Canada today. Canadians have rated it as their most important concern, ahead of programmes in employment and social welfare. In their ten-country study, Blendon *et al.* (1990) found Canadians to be the nation most satisfied with their system of health care. Today, as governments impose stringent cost controls, some Canadians allege that the quality of health care is beginning to suffer. Yet there is very little support for any change in the basic principles of medicare.

Most Canadians believe that medicare is an essential part of Canada's national identity and part of their own individual understanding of what it means to be Canadian. Politicians of every party routinely profess their dedication to keeping medicare alive and healthy. Its growth and development are a reflection of the complex interactions between the federal and provincial powers, a dynamic that continues to unfold.

In this paper I intend to trace the development of medicare, especially as it relates to the evolving federal-provincial dynamic. I rely on Taylor (1986) for his comprehensive review of this topic up to 1984, and Wilson (1999) for a more recent update. We began with the *British North America Act*. The Act gave control of health and social programmes to the provinces, but gave the taxing power to the federal government. The government then declared an "overriding interest" in health, education and social welfare and used its spending power to create national programmes and to control the conditions governing them in areas of provincial jurisdiction. The evolution of health care and social programmes in Canada is a reflection of a continuing struggle between the provinces' desire for autonomy and the federal government's interest in the creation of national programmes. The spending power was essential for the creation of these programmes. The current medicare programme is perhaps the best example of fifty years of provincial-federal negotiations in this contentious area. This evolution is outlined in Table 1.

Table 1: Medicare and Canadian Federalism

1867	– *The British North America Act*
1947	– The Saskatchewan CCF government introduced universal hospital insurance: The *Saskatchewan Hospitalization Act* — the first universal hospital insurance act in North America.
1948	– National Health Grants Programme — the first federal initiative in health care.
1956	– *The Federal Hospital Insurance and Diagnostic Services Act* (HIDS) was passed.
1961	– Saskatchewan under the leadership of Tommy Douglas initiated a provincial medical insurance programme — another first in North America.
1964	– The Royal Commission on Health Services (The Hall Commission) endorsed a comprehensive range of benefits that would be federally subsidized and provincially administered. *The Medical Care Insurance Act*, passed in 1966, went into effect in 1968.
1977	– The *Established Programs Financing Act* became operational, a radical change, from cost-sharing to block-funding for hospital, health care and education.
1979-80	– The Health Services Review (Hall Commission).
1981	– House of Commons Task Force Report *Fiscal Federalism in Canada.*
1984	– Canadian Medical Association. Task Force on Health Care Resources.
1984	– *Canada Health Act* forbids extra-billing and user fees.
1995	– The *Canada Health and Social Transfer* (CHST).
1999	– A Framework to Improve the Social Union for Canadians.

Efforts at hospital and health insurance in the early decades of the 1900s consisted of voluntary pre-payment efforts such as friendly societies, mining companies and railway employees contracts, and the beginnings of commercial insurance. Saskatchewan and Alberta had both municipal doctor and hospital programmes.

In 1939, the Depression and war pushed the issue of public health insurance onto the national political agenda. A proposal for federal subsidies to provincially administered programmes was presented to the House of Commons Select Committee on Social Security in 1943. The proposal was endorsed by labour, farmers' and women's groups, by the Canadian Medical Association and the Life Insurance industry. A 1944 Gallup Poll showed that 80 per cent of the Canadian adult population wanted, and were willing to pay for a comprehensive national health programme.

The federal government, at a special Dominion-Provincial Conference on Post-War Reconstruction in August 1945, offered subsidies to the provinces to support the introduction of health insurance. The proposal was based on a funding formula that ensured that over time the bulk of the costs would be borne by the provinces. The price was more than the provinces were willing to pay and the proposal failed.

The vacuum in the health field was entered by the commercial insurance companies and by the creation and expansion of medical profession-sponsored and controlled pre-payment plans. By 1952 more than five million Canadians were insured for varying degrees of hospital insurance and four million had some degree of protection against medical and surgical costs.

In January 1947, the Saskatchewan Co-Operative Commonwealth Federation (CCF) government introduced a universal hospital insurance: *The Saskatchewan Hospitalization Act*, the first universal hospital insurance Act in North America. The CCF was a farmer-labour-socialist coalition led by the charismatic Tommy Douglas, who led the party to power in Saskatchewan in 1944. Complete health-care coverage was a major plank of the CCF's platform from its inception.

The first federal initiative in health care came in 1948, the National Health Grants Programme. It provided aid to provinces for health professional training, health surveys and hospital construction, and was a great stimulus to hospital construction. It essentially laid the framework for what was to come later.

At the 1955 Conference on Tax Agreements, Premier Leslie Frost of Ontario proposed a national hospital insurance programme. Prime

Minister Louis St. Laurent opposed the idea, but was pushed by Paul Martin, Minister of National Health and Welfare, who threatened to resign if the federal Cabinet did not support the proposal. St. Laurent reluctantly agreed. In January 1956 the federal *Hospital Insurance and Diagnostic Services Act* (HIDS) was passed. It was a shared-cost programme with the provinces which had to meet certain federal conditions: universal coverage, comprehensive in-patient services at standard ward level, portability of benefits, and availability on equal terms and conditions to all provincial residents. These were the basic conditions that were to govern all subsequent cost-sharing health insurance programmes. Thus, in 1958 a national, provincially-administered hospital insurance programme was born.

Once this cost-sharing programme came into effect, Saskatchewan was able to make its next great leap forward. In 1961, Saskatchewan, under the leadership of Douglas, initiated a provincial medical insurance programme, another first in North America. This Act covered all "medically necessary services" outside hospital. The medical profession was bitterly opposed to this legislation and intervened massively in the provincial election, but the public supported the government. Despite a doctors' strike which crippled medical care for one month, the programme began operation in August 1962. Following the recommendations of the Hall Commission, the federal government provided the resources to make a national programme possible (*Medical Care Insurance Act*, 1966).

The initial funding was by fifty/fifty cost-sharing, under strict federal supervision. The provinces resented the rigid controls and the inability to make local adaptations for their own health needs. The federal government felt it had lost control of its own budget because of the rising cost of the programmes. This led to the *Established Programmes Financing Act* of 1977, a radical change from open-ended cost-sharing to defined block-funding for hospital insurance, healthcare insurance and post-secondary education. The provinces gained some autonomy, but became responsible for any government cost overruns, and the federal government had better control over its own spending, but also gave up some control over the programmes.

With the passage of time there was mounting public concern that the provinces were diverting funds intended for health care to other provincial programmes, and that they were permitting extra-billing and user fees which threatened free access to the medicare system. The federally appointed Health Services Review (Hall Commission) was charged with investigating these concerns and the report recommended strongly against extra-billing and user fees. This was further buttressed by the House of Commons Task Force Report which defined the role of the federal government as overseer of national programmes with the obligation to enforce and, if necessary, punish infractions. The *Canada Health Act, 1984* forbade these practices and imposed penalties.

With rising health-care costs, and a rising national deficit, the federal government moved to reduce its contributions progressively following 1977, putting the provinces under severe financial pressure. This culminated in the Canada Health and Social Transfer in 1995, when the government cut $6.5 billion of federal transfer monies over a two-year period while still forcing the provinces to abide by the terms of the *Canada Health Act*. The net result was a draconian cut in health services. Hospital budgets were slashed, services and beds cut, and many hospitals closed. Waiting lists for surgery became increasingly longer and patients had to wait months, even years for elective surgery. There was widespread dissatisfaction among physicians which resulted in the loss of some highly trained specialists to the United States. Despite their unhappiness with what was going on, the majority of Canadians were still opposed to making any basic change in the structure of medicare. The provinces felt that the federal government had abandoned its support for medicare and was deflecting public criticism onto the provinces.

Federal cost retrenchment and a general improvement in the economy led the government to restore some of the funding in the 1999 budget. The federal and provincial governments were unhappy with the state of affairs and both put their senior officials to work to attempt a resolution of the conflict. The result was the "Framework to Improve the Social Union for Canadians" signed in 1999, under which the federal government agreed to a co-operative form of federalism, which meant that no new national programmes could be undertaken without the consent of the provinces. Provinces could opt out and still receive their share of programme funding as long as they agreed to spend it on analogous programmes of their own. Finally, health-care funding would be restored to 1995 levels, but must be spent on health-care programmes, and the *Canada Health Act* would become more negotiable.

CONCLUSIONS

The development of the Canadian health-care system has been marked by the making of small changes and building on the past over a fifty-year period. However, incrementalism was punctuated by two explosive steps: the introduction by Saskatchewan's CCF government of the *Saskatchewan Hospital Insurance* plan, 1947 and the *Medical Care Insurance Act,* 1961, the first universal hospital and medical insurance Acts in North America. In each instance it was followed by federal legislation extending the principles to the entire country. Movement toward national goals was slow. The political process was characterized by a continuing struggle between the provincial and federal officials over structure, function and fiscal responsibilty for the programmes. Yet, in the end it is remarkable how rational were the outputs of the political bargains on health insurance.

How did we come up with a system so different from that in the United States? The *British North America Act* spelled out provincial powers, but left vast residual powers with the federal government, while the reverse was true in the United States. Thus, there are fewer leverage points in the Canadian than in the American system (one Minister and the Cabinet are ultimately responsible). The Canadian public was unwavering in its support for government-supported medical care and there were many dedicated and committed Canadian politicians who strongly supported it. In the end it was Canada's greater "collectivism" along with a mixture of democratic socialism and "red Toryism" which made medicare a reality. Medicare and other social programmes have become a central part of Canadian-self identification and pride.

REFERENCES

Blendon, R.J. *et al.* (1990), "Satisfaction with Health Systems in Ten Nations", *Health Affairs* 9 (Summer):187-192.

Taylor, M.J. (1986), "The Canadian Health Care System, 1974-84", in *Medicare at Maturity*, ed. R.G. Evans and G.L. Stoddart, Calgary: Banff Centre for Continuing Education, University of Calgary Press.

Wilson, K. (1999), "The Changing Federal Role in Health Care", *Annals of the Royal College of Physicians and Surgeons of Canada* 32(1):13-17.

CHAPTER 19

Accountability in Public Health

G.H. Reynolds

INTRODUCTION

On February 21, 1998, President Clinton announced a new initiative that committed the United States to the goal that the country eliminate, by the year 2010, the disparities in six areas of health status experienced by racial and ethnic minority populations while continuing the progress made in improving the overall health of the American people. The Department of Health and Human Services responded by saying that this would require a major national commitment to address the underlying causes and to deliver more effectively both preventive and clinical services. They felt that these causes included poverty, lack of access to quality health services, environmental hazards and the need for effective prevention programmes. And these, of course, are all related to the histories of non-white groups in the United States, including the legacies of slavery, genocide, apartheid and persistent economic and social inequality: especially in education, employment opportunity, housing and health care. The differences in health outcomes between the racial/ethnic groups are not fixed. In this paper, I show that there is great heterogeneity within and between racial/ethnic groups. The disparities occur between these groups within each state and for each specific racial/ethnic group between states. The following figures demonstrate disparities for the areas of infant mortality and other causes of death, but these disparities exist for each racial/ethnic group for all the major causes of death. The figures show the state (or District of Columbia) with the highest rate and the one with the lowest rate for each racial and ethnic group and the U.S. average for infant mortality. Data were obtained from the National Vital Statistics System (National Center for Health Statistics, 1996; National Center for Chronic Disease Prevention and Health Promotion, 1997).

INFANT MORTALITY

Figure 1 shows infant mortality rates for the United States, Massachusetts (the state with the lowest rate of infant mortality for black Americans, 10.2 per 1,000 live births) and Washington, D.C. (which has the highest rate for black Americans, 18.9 per 1,000 live births) for 1995-96. In the United States overall, the infant mortality rate for black Americans is more than two times that of white Americans, Hispanic Americans and Asian/Pacific Islanders. The national average for black Americans is 14.4 per 1,000 live births. The infant mortality rates for black infants are lowest in Massachusetts (10.2), Nebraska (11.5), Nevada (10.6), Oregon (11.3), Texas (10.8) and Kentucky (11.8). The highest rates are in Illinois (18.0), Indiana (16.3), Iowa (17.6), Kansas (17.7), Pennsylvania (16.5) West Virginia (16.8) and Wisconsin (17.5). In all figures the zero does not mean the rate is zero, it means that the number of deaths was too small and so the rates are unstable. The rates

Figure 1: Black Infant Mortality Rates: United States and
          Selected States, 1995-1996

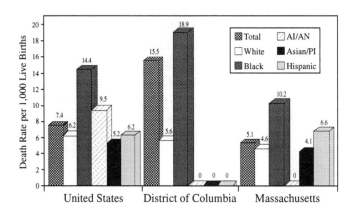

Notes: 0 indicates that numbers were too small, making the rate unstable.
       States selected — one with highest rate and one with lowest rate
       for black infants.

Source: Centers for Disease Control and Prevention.

for infant mortality in the American Indian/American Native (AI/AN) and Hispanic groups were unstable in the District of Columbia, as was the rate for AI/AN in Massachusetts.

Figure 2 shows the states with the highest and lowest infant mortality rates for AI/AN. Minnesota has a rate of 19.1 per 1,000 live births and New Mexico has a rate of 7.2, almost a three-fold difference. There is much less disparity in New Mexico in infant mortality rates between the racial/ethnic groups than in Minnesota. Minnesota and Pennsylvania have the highest and lowest infant death rates per 1,000 live births for Asian/Pacific Island children (Figure 3). However, the difference is not as great. For Hispanic Infants (Figure 4), Arkansas and Nevada have the highest and lowest infant death rates respectively, almost a 2.5-fold difference.

Arkansas has the highest mortality rate and Massachusetts has the lowest for white infants. Overall, for all racial/ethnic groups there is a tremendous range in infant mortality rates, from approximately four in Asian/Pacific Islanders in Massachusetts and Pennsylvania to approximately eighteen per 1,000 live births in a number of states and the District of Columbia for black and AI/AN infants (Figure 5).

Figure 2: Infant Mortality: United States and Selected States, 1995-1996

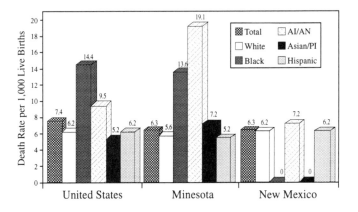

Notes: 0 indicates that numbers were too small, making the rate unstable. States selected — one with highest rate and one with lowest rate for infants.

Source: Centers for Disease Control and Prevention.

Figure 3: Asian/Pacific Island Infant Mortality Rates:
United States and Selected States, 1995-1996

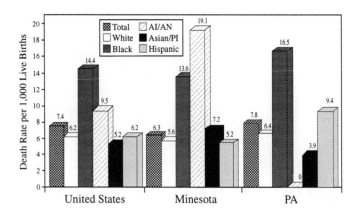

Notes: 0 indicates that numbers were too small, making the rate unstable.
States selected — one with highest rate and one with lowest rate
for Asian/Pacific infants.

Source: Centers for Disease Control and Prevention.

Figure 4: Hispanic Island Infant Mortality Rates:
United States and Selected States, 1995-1996

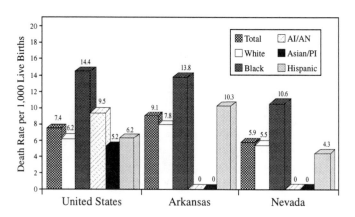

Notes: 0 indicates that numbers were too small, making the rate unstable.
States selected — one with highest rate and one with lowest rate
for Hispanic infants.

Source: Centers for Disease Control and Prevention.

Figure 5: White Infant Mortality Rates: United States and
Selected States, 1995-1996

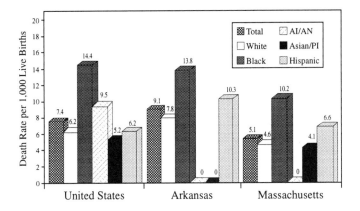

Notes: 0 indicates that numbers were too small, making the rate unstable.
States selected — one with highest rate and one with lowest rate
for white infants.

Source: Centers for Disease Control and Prevention.

DIABETES

When diabetes is the underlying cause of death, similar shifts/
differences by state occur for each of the racial/ethnic groups. The
data did not include breakdowns for the Hispanic population. The age-
adjusted death rate from diabetes in black Americans in West Virginia
(the state with the highest rate) is 2.5 times the death rate for black
Americans in Mississippi (the state with the lowest rate). For those in
West Virginia, the death rate is three times the death rate for white
Americans. Figure 6 also shows that in the United States, the age-
adjusted death rate per 100,000 persons for diabetes as the underlying
cause of death for Blacks and AI/AN is over three times the death rate
for Asian/Pacific Islanders and over two times the death rate in white
Americans. However, for AI/AN, the death rate due to diabetes in South
Dakota is five times the death rate in California (Figure 7). Pacific
Island Americans die from diabetes in Maryland 2.5 times more often
than in Illinois (Figure 8).

Figure 6: For Black Americans: Diabetes as Underlying Cause of
Death: United States and Selected States

Age-Adjusted Rates per 100,000 Persons: Average for 1995

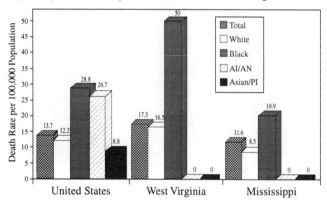

Notes: 0 indicates that numbers were too small, making the rate unstable.
States selected — one with highest rate and one with lowest rate
for Americans.

Source: Centers for Disease Control and Prevention.

Figure 7: Diabetes as Underlying Cause for AI/AN Mortality Rates:
United States and Selected States

Age-Adjusted Rates per 100,000 Persons: Average for 1995

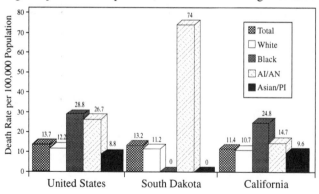

Notes: 0 indicates that numbers were too small, making the rate unstable.
States selected — one with highest rate and one with lowest rate
for AI/AN Americans.

Source: Centers for Disease Control and Prevention.

Figure 8: Diabetes as Underlying Cause for Asian/Pacific Islands
Mortality Rates: United States and Selected States

Age-Adjusted Rates per 100,000 Persons: Average for 1995

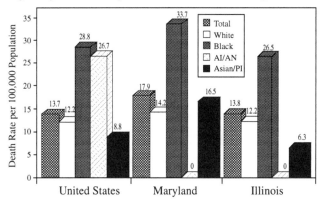

Notes: 0 indicates that numbers were too small, making the rate unstable.
States selected — one with highest rate and one with lowest rate
for Asian/Pacific Island Americans.

Source: Centers for Disease Control and Prevention.

OTHER CAUSES OF DEATH

There is almost a seven-fold difference in age-adjusted death rates
for unintentional injuries between the state with the highest death rate
(South Dakota) and the state with the lowest death rate (California) for
AI/AN; see Figure 9. The state with the highest age-adjusted death
rate for Asian/Pacific Islanders for suicide is Hawaii and the state with
lowest rate is Florida (Figure 10). Surprisingly, although Hawaii in
general has lower death rates for its total population than the U.S. population, it is the state that often has the highest death rates among the
Asian/Pacific Island population for cancer, colorectal cancer, lung cancer, breast cancer, cirrhosis, unintentional injuries, suicide and HIV
infection.

The death rate for Hispanics for coronary heart disease in Arizona is
6.5 times the death rate in Maryland (Figure 11). For AI/AN the death
rate for coronary heart disease in Michigan is almost four times the
death rate in California (Figure 12).

Figure 9:   Unintentional Injuries Causing AI/AN Mortality Rates:
            United States and Selected States

Age-Adjusted Rates per 100,000 Persons: Average for 1993-1995

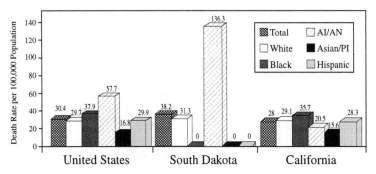

Notes: 0 indicates that numbers were too small, making the rate unstable.
        States selected — one with highest rate and one with lowest rate
        for AI/AN Americans.

Source: Centers for Disease Control and Prevention.

Figure 10: Suicide as Cause for Asian/Pacific Island American
            Mortality Rates: United States and Selected States

Age-Adjusted Rates per 100,000 Persons: Average for 1993-1995

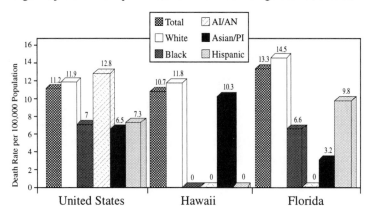

Notes: 0 indicates that numbers were too small, making the rate unstable.
        States selected — one with highest rate and one with lowest rate
        for Asian/Pacific Island Americans.

Source: Centers for Disease Control and Prevention.

Figure 11: Coronary Heart Disease as Cause of Mortality Rates for
Hispanic Americans: United States and Selected States

Age-Adjusted Rates per 100,000 Persons: Average for 1993-1995

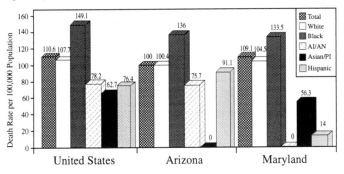

Notes: 0 indicates that numbers were too small, making the rate unstable.
States selected — one with highest rate and one with lowest rate
for Hispanic Americans.

Source: Centers for Disease Control and Prevention.

Figure 12: Coronary Heart Disease as Cause of Mortality Rates for
United States and Selected States

Age-Adjusted Rates per 100,000 Persons: Average for 1993-1995

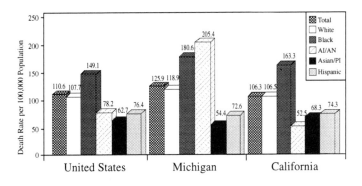

Notes: 0 indicates that numbers were too small, making the rate unstable.
States selected — one with highest rate and one with lowest rate
for AI/AN Americans.

Source: Centers for Disease Control and Prevention.

We have known about these disparities for decades. Why do they continue to exist and even increase for some diseases? What are the barriers to eliminating these disparities and who is accountable?

Multiple Causes

Just as the disparities vary by state, the causes vary by state. The causes can also vary for each racial/ethnic group and for subgroups of these major groups. Thus, many different persons may be involved in responding to health needs for the different minority groups. Minority populations in different states may have had very different educational backgrounds when they came to the United States. Language barriers may exist, making it more difficult to understand where disparities occur and thus to take appropriate action. States may not have the same resources and commitment. When many agencies are involved and/or accountable it may mean no one is accountable.

Poverty and Health

The relationship between poverty and health is complex. The continued and pervasive effects of poverty on health are well known (Ben-Shlomo, White and Marmot, 1996; Gann, Kaplan and Camacho, 1997; Gornick, Eggers, Reilly, Mentnech, Fitterman, Kucken and Vladeck, 1996; Lantz, House, Lepowski, Williams, Mero and Chen, 1998), For blacks, American Indians and Hispanic persons, approximately 30 per cent are living in poverty. And for persons less than eighteen years of age, the percentage living in poverty is even higher (Reynolds, 1996). Access to health care in the United States also varies for different age groups and for different states. Poor people, young people, people born in foreign countries and minorities are all less likely to have health insurance. The percentage of people who are living below the poverty level ranged from 6.9 per cent in New Hampshire to 24 per cent in New Mexico for the three-year average, 1995-97 (Dalaker and Naifeh, 1997). In the United States, 45.4 per cent of poor persons between the ages of eighteen to twenty-four, 47.5 per cent of poor persons between the ages of twenty-five to thirty-four, and 43.8 per cent of poor persons between the ages of thirty-five to forty-four had no health insurance coverage in 1997 (Bennefield, 1997).

The percentage of people with health insurance varies from state to state. This affects health-care access and outcomes. Under Medicaid, the programme that provides medical assistance for certain individuals and families with low incomes and resources, each of the states, within broad national guidelines which the federal government provides, establishes its own eligibility requirements, determines the type, amount, duration and scope of services, sets the rate of payment for services and administers its own programme. Thus, the programme varies from state to state, as well as within each state over time. Data from the Census Bureau indicate that even with Medicaid, a number of states: Arizona, Arkansas, Louisiana, Nevada, New Mexico, Oklahoma and Texas had rates between 20 and 25 per cent of children between the ages of zero and eighteen who were without health insurance for the three-year average, 1995-97. Because eligibility for Medicaid for poor children or poor mothers with dependent children is based on income, the working poor may be even less likely to have health insurance than the really very poor. In 1997, 31.2 per cent of white children, 55.6 per cent of black children, 33 per cent of Asian/Pacific Island children, and 60.9 per cent of Hispanic children either had no health insurance or were covered by Medicaid (Bennefield, 1997).

Maldistribution of Wealth

There have been a number of studies in the United Kingdom and the United States that show that not only is health outcome related to poverty, but it is also related to how wealth is distributed in a society (Kaplan, Pamuk, Lynch, Cohen and Balfour, 1996; Kennedy, Kawachi, Glass and Prothrow-Stith, 1998; Lynch and Kaplan,1997; Smith, 1996; Wilkinson, 1992 and 1994). The greater the maldistribution of wealth, the poorer the health outcomes. In the United States, 1 per cent of the richest people own more wealth than the bottom 90 per cent (Kennickell, McMaanus and Woodburn,1996; Kennickell and Woodburn,1997). Politically, the redistribution of income/wealth to enable all people to earn a reasonable living wage will be very difficult.

Differences in Health Care Received by Blacks

In addition to poverty, lack of access to health care and the maldistribution of wealth, there have been a number of studies that have documented differences in the health care received by white and black patients even when they were under the same health-care system such as the Veteran's Administration hospitals or Medicare (Aeonian, 1993; Becker, Han, Meyer, Wright, Rhodes, Smith, Barrett and the CPR Chicago Project,1993; Whittle, Conigliaro, Good and Lofgren,1993). There are studies, for example, that show that black Americans are having worse outcomes than white Americans because they have "lesser" access to care and even when the treatment is provided in settings where there should be no financial incentive for physicians to use procedures more often in persons with insurance. The differences were very similar to other studies. Thus, financial incentives do not explain this even if one were to consider them to be an excuse for disparate treatment.

HEALTH POLICY AND THE POLITICAL ARENA

Finally and most importantly, health policy takes place in the political arena. Decisions about the provision of health and who is served are political decisions. Data about health outcomes are often interpreted through the perceptions of the target group by those making the decisions to provide affordable care. Identifying the causes of these problems is a political issue. Health problems should be defined, understood and addressed in their historical, economic and social contexts. If that happens, then "accountability in public health" would mean not only admitting particular historical inequities, but actually addressing them in this context. Priorities and decisions about areas to fund, problems to study, and how to address the problems, are based on understanding the problems.

CONCLUSION

Presenting data on health outcomes, poverty and health insurance coverage for each racial and ethnic group by state allows us to look at the causes from a societal perspective and helps to illuminate the underlying causes. The economic and political structures that present barriers to equality in health-care access can be identified and can provide information on how to change and/or remove the structural and institutional barriers. It should help in directing resources to states with the highest death rates and those groups with the highest death rates within a state. Statisticians can contribute to a better understanding of the causes of disparities in the different populations and geographic areas by working with the minority communities to ensure that we:

(i) ask the right questions; (ii) collect, analyze and disseminate the data as completely as possible; (iii) develop and evaluate appropriate interventions and work with the community to interpret and disseminate the results to those at risk and to policy-makers at all levels.

REFERENCES

Aeonian, J.Z. (1993), "Heart Disease in Black and White", *New England Journal of Medicine* 329: 656-658.

Becker, L.B., Han, B.H., Meyer, P.B., Wright, F.A., Rhodes, K.V., Smith, D.W., Barrett, J. and the CPR Chicago Project (1993), "Racial Differences in the Incidence of Cardiac Arrest and Subsequent Survival", *New England Journal of Medicine* 329: 600-606.

Bennefield, R.L. (1997) "Health Insurance Coverage:1997", *Current Population Reports,* Washington, D.C.: U.S. Department of Commerce, pp. 1-7.

Ben-Shlomo, Y., White, I.R. and Marmot, M. (1996), "Does the Variation in the Socioeconomic Characteristics of an Area Affect Mortality?" *British Medical Journal* 312: 1013-1014.

Dalaker, J. and Naifeh, M. (1997), "Poverty in the United States:1997", *Current Population Reports: Consumer Income*, Washington, D.C.: U.S. Department of Commerce, pp. 60-201.

Gaan, M., Kaplan, G.A. and Camacho, T. (1997), "Poverty and Health Prospective Evidence from the Alameda County Study", *American Journal of Public Health* 125:989-998.

Gornick, M.El, Eggers, P.W., Reilly, T.W., Mentnech, R.M., Fitterman, L.K., Kucken, L.E. and Vladeck, B.C. (1996), "Effects of Race and Income on Mortality and Use of Services Among Medicare Beneficiaries", *New England Journal of Medicine* 335:791-799.

Kaplan G., Pamuk, E., Lynch, J.W., Cohen, R.D. and Balfour, J.L (1996), "Inequality in Income and Mortality in the United States: Analysis of Mortality and Potential Pathways", *British Medical Journal* 312:999-1003.

Kennedy, B.P., Kawachi, I., Glass, R. and Prothrow-Stith, D. (1998), "Income Distribution, Socioeconomic Status, and Self-Rated Health in the United States: Multi-level Analysis", *British Medical Journal* 317:917-921.

Kennickell, A. B. and Woodburn, R.L. (1997), "Consistent Weight Design for the 1989, 1992, and 1995 SCFs, and the Distribution of Wealth", Mimeo, Washington, D.C.: Federal Reserve Board.

Kennickell, A. B., McMaanus, D.A., and Woodburn, R.L. (1996), "Weighting Design for the 1992 Survey of consumer Finances", Mimeo, Washington, D.C.: Federal Reserve Board.

Lantz, P.M., House, J.S., Lepowski, J.M., Williams, D.R., Mero, R.P. and Chen, J. (1998), "Socioeconomic Factors, Health Behaviors, and Mortality", *Journal of the American Medical Association* 279:1703-1708.

Lynch, J.W. and Kaplan, G.A. (1997), "Understanding how Inequality in the Distribution of Income Affects Health", *Journal of Health Psychology* 2:297-314.

National Center for Chronic Disease Prevention and Health Promotion (CDC), (1997), *National Vital Statistics System*, Data computed by Surveillance Section, Division of Diabetes Translation.

National Center for Health Statistics (1996), *National Vital Statistics System*, Data computed by Division of Health Promotion Statistics, Hyattsville, MD: U.S. Department of Health and Human Services.

Reynolds, G.H. (1996), "Discussion on Session on Statistical Issues in Minority Health", *1996 Proceedings of the Epidemiology Section, ASA*, pp. 16-18.

Smith, G.D. (1996), "Income Inequality and Morality: Why Are They Related?" *British Medical Journal* 312:987-988.

Whittle, J., Conigliaro, J., Good, C.B. and Lofgren, R.P. (1993), "Racial Differences in the Use of Invasive Cardiovascular Procedures in the Department of Veterans Affairs Medical System", *New England Journal of Medicine* 329: 621-627.

Wilkinson, R.G. (1992), "Income Distribution and Life Expectancy", *British Medical Journal* 304: 165-168.

————— (1994), *Unhealthy Choices: The Affiliations of Inequality*, London: Routledge.

CHAPTER 20

Progress in Research: Applied versus Basic Science in Statistics and Medicine

E.A. Gehan

INTRODUCTION

Howard E. Skipper delineated the place of the statistician among the scientific disciplines: "The ranking or 'social status' of an individual or group of individuals in a general research area is inversely proportional to the size of the particle on which he works" (Skipper, 1962). With this as a standard, Skipper ordered the disciplines as follows: theoretical mathematician, nuclear physicist, physical chemist, organic chemist, biochemist, virologist and geneticist, microbiologist, pathologist, pharmacologist and clinician. He then rated statisticians next to the theoretical mathematicians on the scale, since they are "first or second cousins to theoretical mathematicians". Humanists were not included in this rating of scientific disciplines, but clearly members of that discipline should be rated highly, since their work derives mainly from their mental capabilities.

I wish to pursue a corollary to Skipper's philosophy, namely that an applied scientist tends to be rated lower than a basic scientist in the same field. The theme suggests that there should be an equivalent ranking for applied and basic scientists or the order should be reversed since new developments in basic science often evolve from the applied sciences and not the other way around. Since I am a biostatistician, I shall explore this concept for the fields of medicine and statistics.

APPLIED VERSUS BASIC SCIENCE

There is a general perception that working in the basic sciences is superior to working in the applied sciences. Consider the following pairs of words: curiosity/need, academic/industry, principles/practices, fundamentals/implementation and understanding/processes. All of the words listed first in each pair have "positive associations" and are associated with basic scientists while the second in each pair, while not necessarily negative are clearly less positive and associated with applied scientists. Generally, knowledge of first principles and having a fundamental understanding of a research project have a higher perceived status than the merely practical implementation of a process, even when it may benefit mankind.

APPLIED VERSUS BASIC RESEARCH IN MEDICINE

Differing Views

At a recent panel discussion sponsored by the National Institutes of Health (NIH), the chairman of the committee appointed to stimulate clinical research stated the following:

> I want NIH [National Institute of Health] to support the most promising research no matter what it is. I know from my own life experience that basic research provides all the ideas for medical research. If you don't have tons of basic research going on, you never get any ideas for clinical research (Nathan, 1997, p. 261).

This point was reiterated further when Dr. Harold Varmus, the current Director of NIH, was selected for a very important position, President of the Memorial Sloan Kettering Cancer Institute in New York City. A primary item on his agenda may be paraphrased as "To build up the basic research capability of the staff members so that innovative projects can be designed in clinical research" (*New York Times*, October 1999). These viewpoints differ from those of others who believe that progress in science derives from applications that drive developments in basic research. For example, W. B. Castle was a distinguished hematologist who made a major contribution to the treatment of pernicious liver anemia in the 1920s. He discovered a specific intrinsic factor that provided a key to developing a curative treatment for liver anemia. He believed that progress in medicine is derived from observant, intelligent clinicians. He wrote: "His is a front-line position in the advance of knowledge concerning disease, for the flow of discovery is almost always from man towards the molecule. If occasionally the direction is reversed, it is a sequence secondary to the other" (Castle, 1976).

Crisis in Clinical Investigations

Beginning in the 1970s and continuing to the present, a crisis has been reported in the conduct of clinical investigations, the result being that clinicians are no longer at the forefront of clinical investigations. Instead, basic scientists have taken leadership roles in the conduct of clinical investigations and as leaders of medical institutions. In designing clinical trials, it has become more important for the principal investigator to have a Ph.D. rather than an M.D. degree. Titles of some recent lectures indicate the nature of the problem: "Who Took the Clinical Out of Clinical Research" by E. Freireich (1997); "The Clinical Investigator as an Endangered Species, by J.B. Wyngaarden (1979) and "The Clinical Cancer Researcher: Still an Embattled Species by E. Frei (1993). As the then Director of the National Institutes of Health, Wyngaarden was in a very good position to know about the problem. A recent text, *The Crisis in Clinical Research* by E. H. Ahrens, Jr. (1992), is a further illustration.

A quantitative measure of the problem is given by the following. In 1997, there were about 16,300 applications for research grants submitted to NIH by Ph.D.s, of which about 5,000 (31 per cent) were funded. By comparison, those with M.D. degrees submitted only about 5,800 research grant applications and approximately 1,850 (32 per cent) were awarded. Hence, though the award rate was about the same for M.D.s and Ph.D.s, a much larger number of Ph.D. applications led to many more grants with the Ph.D. as principal investigator. Since 1970, research grants proposed by Ph.D.s have approximately tripled, from about 5,000 to over 16,000 in 1997. In contrast, the growth in research grant applications from M.D.s has grown only about 75 per cent, from about 1,300 in 1970 to about 2,300 in 1997.

First-time applications for NIH research-project grant awards have been declining since 1994 to a current level of about 600, whereas those with Ph.D.s in medicine have remained relatively constant at about 200. The trend since 1994 indicates a continuing decrease for M.D. applicants for research grants.

Statistically, there is fairly strong evidence that there are fewer physicians pursuing research careers than before. Nearly 15 per cent of graduating medical students had strong research career intentions in 1987 and this has declined steadily to slightly over 10 per cent in 1996. Of those receiving post-doctoral research training or fellowships in 1996, over 70 per cent were Ph.D.s and less than 30 per cent were M.D.s.

There has been an increasing growth in subspecialties versus general medical societies. The Association of American Physicians (since 1890), the American Society for Clinical Investigation (since 1910) and the American Federation for Clinical Research (since 1920) constitute the three major general medical societies. Registration at their meetings has decreased markedly from over 4,000 in 1986 to slightly over 1,000 in 1998. At the same time, attendance at subspecialty society meetings has grown substantially over the same period. For example, the American Society of Clinical Oncology has increased from an attendance of about 2,000 in 1991 to over 14,000 in 1997. Many of those attending the subspecialty meetings have Ph.D.s rather than M.D.s. The number of abstracts submitted for the tri-society meetings decreased from nearly 3,000 in 1986 to less than five hundred in 1998. However, there has been substantial growth in the number of abstracts submitted for the subspecialty meetings. For example, for the American Society of Clinical Oncology meetings, the number of abstracts has increased from about eight hundred in 1991 to over 2,000 in 1997. In a reaction to Ph.D.s dominating clinical research, a new society was formed by a group of M.D.s,"The Association for Patient-Oriented Research", and a successful meeting was held in Atlantic City, New Jersey, in May 1999.

Medicine Becomes more Scientific in the Twentieth Century

Prior to 1900, physicians did not rely on scientific principles in deciding about treatments for patients. There was much more reliance on anecdotal evidence, herbal remedies and, generally, treatments chosen for their effects on symptoms, rather than science-based evidence. The years 1890-1920 saw the formation of medical societies, including the American Association of Physicians, the American Society for Clinical Investigation and the American Foundation for Clinical Research. Clinicians began to meet regularly to discuss new advances. In 1910, the Flexner Report resulted in a more scientific curriculum for medical students. A milestone was reached in the United States in 1947 when the NIH was founded.

I consider now some therapeutic advances in cancer in the twentieth century from the viewpoint of whether the advance derived from work in basic science or was primarily driven by clinical observations. Advances in the latter half of the twentieth century will be discussed briefly. An advance deriving from basic science was the use of methotrexate in the treatment of choriocarcinoma in the mid-1950s and it was the first drug cure of cancer, since approximately 50 per cent of patients were cured (Hertz, Lewis and Lipsett, 1961). Methotrexate was tried because it was recognized that a folate antagonist can act as an anti-neoplastic agent by interfering with one or more bio-synthetic steps involving co-enzymes of the tumor cell. Farber, Diamond, Mecor *et al.* (1948) demonstrated that Methotrexate was effective in producing remissions in acute leukemia.

Subsequently, however, a number of clinical trials built upon these observations by trying combinations of agents that had activity and when the toxicity was not overlapping. For example, Frei, Freireich, Gehan *et al.* (1961) demonstrated that the combination of 6-mecaptopurine and methotrexate yielded a higher complete remission rate than either drug alone and the improved response rate could be explained by the independent action of the two drugs. This led to the use of multiple drug combinations to increase response rates in acute leukemia, Hodgkin's disease, non-Hodgkin's lymphoma, osteosarcoma, testicular cancer, and breast cancer (Table 1). While these trials built upon basic science, the main concept utilized was to combine individually active drugs that had toxicities that were not additive. During the 1960s and 1970s, supportive therapies were refined, including the use of platelet and white cell transfusions and the treatment of patients in protected environments. In the 1970s and 1980s, Bernard Fisher and colleagues of the National Surgery Adjuvant Breast Group (1970, 1985) demonstrated that the radical mastectomy was not necessary for breast cancer patients and he and co-workers pioneered reduced surgery for breast cancer. From the 1970s and into the 1990s, bone marrow transplantation has been used for various types of cancer, including acute leukemia and breast cancer. These advances via clinical trials were made mainly by astute clinicians involved in the actual treatment of patients rather than by scientists in the laboratory suggesting clinical studies.

Table 1:   Some Clinical Trials of New Drugs and Combinations
of Drugs

MTX, Ara-C, VAMP in acute leukemia	Farber *et al.* (1948), Freireich and Frei (1964); Freireich *et al.* (1967).
MOPP in Hodgkin's disease	DeVita, Serpick and Carbone (1970).
CHOP in non-Hodgkin's lymphoma	Gottlieb *et al.* (1973), Rodriquez *et al.* (1977).
Cyclophosphamide in Burkitt's lymphoma	Burkitt (1967).
Adriamycin in soft tissue sarcoma	Gottlieb *et al.* (1972).
CONPADRI in osteosarcoma	Sutow *et al.* (1978).
Velban, bleomycin and cis-platinum testicular cancer	Einhorn and Donohue (1977).
Combination chemotherapy in advanced and early breast cancer	Greenspan (1966); Cooper (1969); Buzdar, Gutterman and Blumenschein (1978).

APPLIED VERSUS BASIC RESEARCH IN STATISTICS

Some milestones in statistics for the period 1900-50 are given in Table 2. Among the group of statisticians, Sir Ronald Fisher and Abraham Wald are the only individuals who would be considered outstanding theoretical statisticians. R. A. Fisher wrote a landmark paper "On the Mathematical Foundations of Theoretical Statistics" (Fisher, 1922), but he also worked closely with agricultural experimenters at the Rothamstead Experiment Station and his work on design of experiments, analysis of variance, and the writing of *Statistical Methods for Research Workers* (Fisher, 1925) derived from his work with applied scientists.

Abraham Wald's work in sequential analysis was a theoretical treatment of the methodology; but in the preface to his book, Wald expressed his indebtedness to Milton Friedman and W. Allen Wallis who proposed

Table 2: Some Milestones in Statistics, 1900-1950

Early 1900s	Contingency tables (K. Pearson)
1908	*t test* (W. S. Gosset)
1912	Maximum likelihood (R. A. Fisher)
1910-1930s	Statistical distribution theory (R. A. Fisher)
1930s	Design of experiments (R. A. Fisher) Analysis of variance Randomization basis of inference "Statistical Methods for Research Workers"
1943	Sequential analysis (A. Wald)
1946	Rank tests (F. Wilcoxon)
1947	Randomized clinical trial (A.B. Hill)

the problem of sequential analysis: "It was their clear formulation of the problem that gave me the incentive to start the investigations leading to the present development" (Wald, 1947).

Among the other statisticians listed, their theoretical advances all derived from applications. W.S. Gosset worked for the Guinness Brewery in Ireland and the t-test was developed as an hypothesis test of the difference between means in small samples. Gosset made an inspired guess about the distribution of *t*, which was later confirmed in a proof by Fisher. F. Wilcoxon spent his career in the pharmaceutical industry and is responsible for rank tests, which are useful for many applications when the data are not normally distributed. A.B. Hill was responsible for the first formally randomized clinical trial in tuberculosis. Though he was a professor of Medical Statistics, his highest degree was a B.Sc. from University College and he certainly did not consider himself a theoretician.

Table 3 lists some milestones in statistics after 1950. What is perhaps most noticeable on this list is that all authors are good theoreticians, but also had strong interests in applications. J. Cornfield worked

Table 3: Some Milestones in Statistics after 1950

Year	Milestone
1951	Estimation of relative risks (J. Cornfield)
1957	Sequential clinical trials (P. Armitage)
1958	Non-parametric life table estimation (E. Kaplan and P. Meier)
1958	Logistic regression analysis (D.R. Cox)
1959	Estimation of summary relative risks (N. Mantel and W. Haenszel)
1972	Generalized linear models (P. McCullagh and J. Nelder)
1972	Semi-parametric regression analysis (D.R. Cox)
1979	Computer intensive statistical methods (B. Efron)
1986	Longitudinal data analysis (K. Liang and S. Zeger)

at the NIH and his work on relative risks was very useful in the analysis and interpretation of case-control studies. P. Armitage followed in the path that Wald had initially broken by applying the theory of sequential analysis to clinical trials, where practical considerations required limiting the total number of observations. N. Mantel worked at the National Cancer Institute throughout his career and worked closely with experimenters, including W. Haenszel who was primarily an epidemiologist.

Perhaps the outstanding milestone in statistics in the latter half of the twentieth century was the development of the proportional hazards regression model by D.R. Cox (1972). Cox, though an outstanding theoretical statistician, has also worked closely with experimenters throughout his career.

In statistics, then, there is strong evidence that progress in the twentieth century has arisen from the close interplay of ideas between theoreticians and applied scientists. In considering the milestones of this century, it was a necessary condition that the discoverers were good at both theory and applications. One without the other was not sufficient.

CONCLUSION

For advances in both medicine and statistics, basic science and applications are both of primary importance. Progress in both medicine and statistics has resulted from the close interplay of ideas between theoreticians and those in applied fields.

REFERENCES

Ahrens, E.H., Jr. (1992), *The Crisis in Clinical Research*, Oxford: Oxford University Press.

Burkitt, D. (1967), "Long-Term Remissions Following One and Two Dose Chemotherapy for African Lymphoma", *Cancer* 20:756-759.

Buzdar, A.U., Gutterman, J.U. and Blumenschein, G. R. (1978), "Intensive Post-Operative Chemoimmunotherapy for Patients with Stage II and III Breast Cancer", *Cancer* 41:1064-1075.

Castle, W.B. (1976), "Physician as Scientist: Preparation, Performance, and Prospects", The Alan Gregg Memorial Lecture, *Journal of Medical Education* 51:39-45.

Cooper, R. (1969), "Combination Chemotherapy in Hormone Resistant Breast Cancer", *Proceedings of the American Association of Cancer Research* 10:15.

Cox, D.R. (1972), "Regression Models and Life Tables (with discussion)", *Journal of the Royal Statistical Society* (B) 34:187-220.

De Vita, V., Serpick, A. and Carbone, P. (1970), "Combination Chemotherapy in the Treatment of Advanced Hodgkin's Disease", *Annals of Internal Medicine* 73:881-895.

Einhorn, L.H. and Donohue, M. (1977), "Cis-diamminedichloroplatinum, Vinblastine, and Bleomycin Combination Chemotherapy in Disseminated Testicular Cancer", *Annals of Internal Medicine* 87:293-298.

Farber, S., Diamond, L.K., Mercer, R. *et al.* (1948), "Temporary Remissions in Acute Leukemia in Children Produced by the Folic Acid Antagonist Aminopterin", *New England Journal of Medicine* 238:787-793.

Fisher, B. (1970), "The Surgical Dilemma in the Primary Therapy of Invasive Breast Cancer: A Critical Appraisal", *Current Problems in Surgery*, 1-53.

Fisher, B., Redmond, C., Fisher, E.R., Bauer, M. *et al.* (1985), "Ten Year Results of a Randomized Clinical Trial Comparing Radical Mastectomy and Total Mastectomy with or without Radiation", *New England Journal of Medicine* 31:674-681.

Fisher, R.A. (1922), "On the Mathematical Foundations of Theoretical Statistics", *Philosophical Transactions* A222:309-368.

_____ (1925), *Statistical Methods for Research Workers*, Edinburgh: Oliver and Boyd.

Frei, E. (1993), "The Clinical Cancer Researcher: Still an Embattled Species", *Journal of Clinical Oncology* 9:1639-1651.

Frei E., Freireich E.J., Gehan, E.A., *et al.* (1961), "Studies of Sequential and Combination Anti-Metabolite Therapy in Acute Leukemia: 6-Mercaptopurine and Methotrexate", *Blood* 18(4):431-454.

Freireich, E.J. (1997), "Who Took the Clinical Out of Clinical Research? – Mouse versus Man", Seventh David A. Karnofsky Memorial Lecture, 1976. *Clinical Cancer Research* 3:2711-2722.

Freireich, E.J., Bodey, G. P., Harris, J. E. and Hart, J. S. (1967), "Therapy for Acute Granulocytic Leukemia", *Cancer Research* 27:2573-2577.

Freireich, E.J. and Frei, E. III (1964), "Recent Advances in Acute Leukemia", in *Progress in Hematology*, ed. C.V. Moore and E.B. Brown, New York: Grune & Stratton, pp. 189-202.

Gottlieb, J.A., Baker, L.H., Quagliana, J.M. *et al.* (1972), "Chemotherapy of Sarcomas with a Combination of Adriamycin and Dimethyl Triazeno Imidazole Carboxamide", *Cancer* 30:1632-1638.

Gottlieb, J.A., Gutterman, J.U., McCredie, K.B. *et al.* (1973), "Chemotherapy of Malignant Lymphomas with Adriamycin", *Cancer Research* 33:3024-3028.

Greenspan, E. (1966), "Combination Cytotoxic Chemotherapy in Advanced Disseminated Breast Cancer", *Journal of the Mt. Sinai Hospital of New York* 33:1-27.

Hertz, R., Lewis, J. and Lipsett, M.B. (1961), "Five Years Experience with the Chemotherapy of Metastatic Choricarcinoma and Related Trophoblastic Tumors in Women", *American Journal of Obstetric Gynecology* 82:631-636.

Nathan, D. (1997), "Report of Clinical Research Panel: NIH Clinical Research Panel makes Progress", *Journal of Investigative Medicine* 46:261.

Rodriguez, V., Bodey, G.P., Freireich, E.J. *et al.* (1978), "Randomized Trial of Protected Environment – Prophylactic Antibiotics in 145 Adults with Acute Leukemia", *Medicine* 57:253-266.

Skipper, H.E. (1962), "The Peck-Order Law of Scientific Status", *Cancer Chemotherapy Reports* 16:587-588.

Sutow, W.W., Gehan, E.A., Dyment, P.G., Vietti, T. and Miale, T. (1978), "Multidrug Adjuvant Chemotherapy for Osteosarcoma: Interim Report of the Southwest Oncology Group Studies", *Cancer Treatment Reports* 62:265-269.

Wald, A. (1947), *Sequential Analysis,* New York: John Wiley & Sons.

Wyngaarden, J.B. (1979), "The Clinical Investigator as an Endangered Species", *New England Journal of Medicine* 301:1254-1259.

PART VII

CULTURE OF THE MEDIA

CHAPTER 21

The Relation between Scientific Interpretation and Political Action: A Two-Way Street

J.C. Bailar, III

INTRODUCTION

The original meaning of the term "statistics" promises a great deal. The word is ultimately derived from the Latin word for "state", in the sense of a nation, and has been defined as the collection, analysis, interpretation and presentation of masses of numerical data. Ultimately, statistics in this sense is the study of political facts and figures.

This definition has little to do with how many professional statisticians use the word today. Although language changes and fields of study change, sometimes rapidly, we have gone astray in making statistics a largely mathematical discipline, with emphasis on probability models and related matters. Our priorities are scrambled. Mathematical statistics is an important tool, but it is not the central tool of statistics. We must return our focus to the thoughtful analysis and interpretation of quantitative data.

THREE EXAMPLES

I will start with three examples. All are health-related, because I know health better than other fields, though the lessons I draw from these examples seem (from less concentrated study of other matters) to be quite general. I have chosen these examples because they have important policy implications and because they may be somewhat less familiar than other major statistical efforts such as a decennial census, monthly estimates of unemployment, or various aspects of our national accounts.

My first example is what has been called the "Gulf War Syndrome", or GWS. This condition has been said to affect many tens of thousands among the 700,000 U.S. veterans of the Gulf War of 1991-92. Gulf War veterans from other countries have expressed similar complaints. Symptoms attributed to the GWS include fatigue, malaise, headaches, bone and joint pain, difficulty sleeping, skin rashes and many other things. However, each of these symptoms may occur rather commonly even in persons who did not serve in that war. Thus the question is immediately transformed, from whether veterans have these symptoms, to whether the frequency and/or severity of their symptoms is greater than in persons similarly situated but not deployed to the Gulf region in that conflict. In particular, there is much concern that this syndrome is a result of some kind of exposure (perhaps chemical, including chemical warfare agents) that was common in the Gulf area at the time these veterans were serving there. The most important policy implications have to do with diagnosis and correct treatment, prevention in possible future conflicts, and compensation for what may be a service-connected condition.

The GWS has been examined in about twenty reports by different broadly based scientific groups, all of which have concluded that there is no satisfactory evidence that the GWS is related to any unique physical exposure. One of these, issued recently by the RAND Corporation and reporting work done for the U.S. Department of Defense, cites some weak evidence that the syndrome might be related to a specific exposure in the Gulf theatre, but also concludes that the evidence does not establish a physical cause for the problem. Given these expert opinions, why is there still so much uncertainty about the cause of GWS and about our society's responses to it? Among the chief difficulties are: the lack of a unified definition of the syndrome (which seems to be whatever any research investigator, or even any veteran, wants to make it at the time), the lack of any suitable control group, and possible differences in reporting of symptoms between persons who do versus those who do not believe they have the syndrome.

The problem of the Gulf War Syndrome is inherently statistical, because we need to know outcomes, and from those, determine risk factors and levels of risk for the occurrence of the GWS. Our understanding about these matters will have substantial impact on the way we deal with veterans of that conflict. I am quite sceptical that any specific chemical exposure is a cause, in part because of evidence that U.S. veterans of every armed conflict that we have been in, at least as far back as the Civil War, have complained of similar sets of symptoms, though we do not have good estimates of their frequency. It further appears that veterans of other nations in other wars have had similar problems. A very active programme of research is looking at many aspects of the GWS, and it is possible that evidence for some identifiable physical cause will emerge, but it is my present impression that the GWS is a version of a more general "war syndrome", or perhaps an even more general "stress syndrome".

My second example has to do with controlling the health effects of automotive emissions. There is solid evidence that very high levels of general air pollution sometimes seen in the past in many countries, particularly related to air that was stagnant over large cities over a long period of time, increased both morbidity and mortality, sometimes drastically. Many cities and countries have had much success in cleaning up the air, and today's questions centre on whether today's reduced pollution levels still have some small, residual effects, and if so whether they merit further remedial action. Specifically, what we would like to know can be cast in a short series of questions: (i) What is getting into the air from various different sources? (ii) How do those emissions translate into personal exposures (including personal variation such as for persons living near a major roadway or indoor versus outdoor locations)? (iii) What effect do those exposures have on human morbidity and mortality? Each of these questions is difficult to answer and the linkages from one to the next are not easily established. The U.S. Environmental Protection Agency (EPA) has responsibility for air quality in the United States, and has constructed a series of rather elaborate statistical models to deal with various aspects of this, including automotive emissions (all classes of trucks as well as automobiles, and all types of fuels). Similar models have been developed in Germany and elsewhere. However, these models estimate emissions and then stop. We must take on faith that emissions translate into exposures, and that exposures translate into adverse health effects. But even emissions are difficult to measure, and there are numerous important matters for which one simply cannot obtain data. For example, few persons would want to have their own cars selected for full testing over a period of several days, and many would not want to have testing instruments in their cars. We do not know how car-owners' perceptions of a particular car's possible problems may affect willingness to submit a car for testing, so that test results may be correct for the cars tested but seriously biased for the population of cars on the road.

Or, we might want to know the effect on engine emissions of some change in the design of a carburetor or a spark plug. The innovations can be put in test engines and their performance examined in detail on the laboratory test bed, or even in the field. But there is no way to tell what might be coming out of an engine built today but still on the road twenty years from now, possibly after it has been poorly maintained or seriously abused.

We might want to estimate or predict the impact of a revised programme of inspection and maintenance of vehicles. Many people are now familiar with the routine, in which we may wait for hours for our cars to be briefly tested and certified as meeting regulatory standards for use on the road. In many states, testing includes sampling of the exhaust, and we blandly, or blindly, assume that those cars that fail to meet the test will either be repaired or taken out of service. There is good evidence that that is not true, at least in the United States, and it seems that about two-thirds of vehicles failing these state-mandated tests simply do not appear again in later testing records. Are the cars moved to another state with lesser or no standards? Are they converted to off-road uses? Are some in fact repaired but not retested? How many are still in regular use, without the certification that the state requires? We do not know. The EPA must model these and many other matters, and use the model to set standards that are known to be very costly, on the assumption that the unmeasured health benefits are likely to exceed the highly visible costs.

Again, this matter is inherently and unavoidably statistical, since it deals with the analysis and interpretation of data, including data not available, which are related to a policy issue of considerable public importance.

A third example has to do with evaluating the impact of "block grants" from the U.S. federal government to states for the purpose of improving public health. Similar distributions are made in many other countries. Evaluation of such programmes is difficult for several reasons. Some of these reasons are that funds from the central government may make up only a small part of what regional or local authorities are already putting into a programme, that impacts for many kinds of public health measures (such as cancer prevention) are long-delayed, and that available data vary widely among the regions within a country, in scope, definitions, sample sizes and quality. A committee of the U.S. National Academy of Sciences recently recommended four guidelines for the assessment of various measures that might be proposed to estimate the impacts of such programmes:

1. Measures should be aimed at a specific objective and be result-oriented.
2. Measures should be meaningful and understandable.
3. Data should be adequate to support the measures.
4. Measures should be valid, reliable and responsive.

The set of measures which can meet all of these criteria is small. Thus, we must rely on limited, non-uniform, data of variable characteristics and uncertain quality. Again, this is a statistical issue, and it has much public importance with respect to those transfers of huge sums from central to regional and local governments.

LESSONS FROM THE EXAMPLES

These examples, and many others in health and in quite unrelated fields, have led me to recognize four features of statistical data available for use in almost any issue that has important policy implications. The first is that the data are likely to be vast. One could fill many shelves, or even libraries, with material relevant to each of my three examples, and the scope of available material for some other problems would be much larger.

Secondly, the data tend to be highly complex, in the sense that the problem involves many different scientific and technical disciplines as well as non-scientific fields, and no one person can be expert in all of them. For example, full understanding of the GWS would require a deep knowledge of military operations, generally, and in the Gulf Theatre; the actual location of troops in the Gulf and their possible exposures; the health-care systems for military personnel and veterans (including medical health record systems) as well as medical care, more generally; toxicology; epidemiology; biostatistics; survey statistics (especially response biases); and many other things. Given that nobody can be expert in all of these simultaneously, how are we to deal with this complex situation? How can we identify all of the needed expertise, mobilize it, support it, and integrate it to solve an important problem?

Thirdly, most of what is available is of poor quality. Review of what is available on each of my three examples and many other topics has shown uniformly that a small amount of good work has been done, but that poor work is far more common, and that someone not expert in the field and appropriately critical could be seriously misled. Even organizing and getting through this mountain of literature, to determine what subset is worth detailed attention, is a daunting task.

Finally, most of what we have is not going to be appropriate anyway. My best example of that is a fourth topic, related to both the GWS and automotive air pollution, which is the use of laboratory experiments to assess human hazards of exposure to chemicals. This is an important activity, and will remain important, because chemical substances are often considered for new uses, and we might hope that they will not be manufactured and made in quantity if they present serious and unrecognized hazards to human health. This means that our understanding of possible health risks must be derived from other sources, before extensive human exposure occurs. The best substitute in biological terms is animal testing. But such laboratory studies have grave limitations. Because of tight limits on the size of experiments, it is necessary to test small numbers of animals at high doses, and one must extrapolate from high to low exposures as well as from animals to humans. There may be additional extrapolations from lifetime exposure to intermittent human exposure, or from one route of administration (such as food) to another (such as inhalation), as well as still other kinds of extrapolations. At the end, these uncertainties are compounded to a level where actual levels of risk to humans, or even whether there is any risk at all, may be very uncertain. Repeated risk assessments of the same hazards quite commonly show differences of three orders of magnitude (one thousand-fold) or greater. I am not recommending that we abandon such risk assessments, which are generally the best we can do, but pointing to some inherent limitations on the precision of the estimates that can be produced. I firmly believe that, despite their problems, it is better to have a reliable summary of what is known, including uncertainties, than to just gaze into a crystal ball.

Consider these four features of data which I find are related to almost any policy issue (vast, complex, of poor quality and off-target) and see if you do not find echoes of them in other fields of endeavour.

These considerations, based on my concern about the relation between statistics and policy, led me to conclude that bias is almost invariably a matter of greater significance than randomness, at least in any context where the outcome matters. Statistics, in its original sense, is inherently an integrative discipline, but that sense has been largely abandoned. We may measure effects rather precisely in any one, small, well-designed research study, but there will inevitably be important differences among separate studies of the same phenomena, we should give substantial attention to what is known about related areas of the subject, and there is always scope for considerable interpretation.

REPRISE

If these four guidelines are common in the use of statistical concepts and data in public policy, what are we to do? The first step is recognition that there really is a problem. A few years ago, I saw a list of, as I recall, thirty-one major statistical agencies in the U.S. federal government. I was surprised and concerned to discover that twenty-nine of the thirty-one directors had little or no identifiable formal advanced training in statistics. If that remains true, we have a serious failure of the statistical profession in general to provide needed training and leadership in matters of great public importance. I do not suggest that any of the twenty-nine directors were unqualified, and some indeed have became superb applied statisticians. However, they have had to acquire their skills from an unnecessarily narrow disciplinary perspective with, generally, a lot of on-the-job experience, that is, the error part of trial-and-error. Early, organized education about major statistical activities, profiting from on-the-job experience of a broad range of earlier applied statisticians, would surely have been in their interest, and in the interest of all of us.

This should not surprise anyone. For many years, academic statistics has focused on mathematical concepts and computation. We do not attract (or attempt to attract) students who will take on major roles in the public sector as they move to their middle and later careers. We do not encourage students or junior faculty members to acquire supervised, practical experience of the kind that one might get from internship in a statistical organization somewhere in government or the private sector. We do not generally recognize professional contributions outside the statistical literature. In short, persons whose primary professional identification is as statisticians have largely turned their backs on the large, real statistical problems that surround us. Instead, we devise elegant little probability models and apply them to elegant little sets of data that, too often, have no consequential significance.

If we continue to define statistics as the collection, analysis, interpretation and presentation of masses of numerical data, we must recognize that the definition applies to many other professions as well. What is unique about statistics is its emphasis on general processes. The discipline of statistics should be focused on such things as asking the right questions in a way that can be answered, developing research protocols, maintaining and improving the quality of data, reducing massive detail to something that can be comprehended, integrating information of different kinds from different sources, applying probability models, and generalizing results, along with many other things.

As statisticians we may become experts in one or more of these, and such skills are portable. What one learns from one problem, in whatever field of endeavour, can readily be transferred to another. From this point of view, we many consider statistics to be what is left after we gather up the whole of science and technology and squeeze out all of the specifics of the disciplines of application, all of the specifics of individual problems, all of the specifics of research methods, and all of the specifics of individual study outcomes. What is left is the matrix of science itself, including the scientific method generally. That matrix can be applied to almost any issue where quantitative data may be of some utility. If statistics, defined this way, is the science of any one thing, it is the science of the scientific method itself.

In short, our academic programmes have failed us. We are not producing the kinds of graduates, at any level, that our nations need. If we truly believe in the glory and power of statistics, we must ask ourselves why we have so much less impact on world affairs than other professions with a similar technical or quantitative focus, such as economics, or geology, or high-energy physics, or applied mathematics. It is not just a matter of numbers of persons, or of bad luck. It is, in a deep sense, our own problem. We can solve it if we have the will.

CHAPTER 22

Science and the Media

S. Strauss

The relationship of the media to science can be summarized by a version of the classic story about a number of blind men who were trying to determine the nature of an elephant by touching the different parts. The man who touched a leg thought the animal was shaped like a tree; the one who touched the trunk thought it was more like a garden hose, and the person holding an ear thought an elephant was shaped like a leaf. The final blind man, after listening to all the previous responses, refused to touch anything. "Tell us what you think it is shaped like," he was asked by the others. "I don't know," he responded, "but I *do* know it is a trick question."

I contend that the most important difference between the media and science is a trick question. It is not, as many people think, that one has a commercial purpose and the other tries to understand nature. It is rather that the two disciplines frame the same information in accordance with very different principles. I also believe that the framing differences reflect a profound chasm that will never be easily overcome; this is because they are based on very different theories of knowledge, what is classically called differing epistemologies. My argument is just that — an argument. For much of the evidentiary basis to it, I simply ask you to rely on your experience as producers of science and consumers of media.

To begin with, there is a different structure to the presentation of information. At the university, where much of the science teaching takes place, the pedagogical model is as follows. The professor knows much or everything about a given topic. The students, however intrinsically smart they are, know less but want to know more. Ergo, the professor tries to raise the students to his level. How much and how quickly the students rise is measured in a variety of ways, but most typically as a series of tests. If the students do not pass the tests, *they* have failed and are to blame for their continued ignorance. The pedagogical model for journalists is very different. We assume our audience knows nothing about what we are writing or presenting, and may not want to change their state of ignorance. As a consequence, we first descend to their base level and try to convince them that there is something they want to learn. It is a descent that must occur each time information is presented, as we do not ever assume they have learned anything. If they are not interested in what we have to say and ignore it, *we*, not they, have failed. Out of these two different pedagogies flows much of what appears different in the presentation of science to scientists and science in the media.

What journalists, and the media in general, believe is that things are best understood and remembered when embedded in a narrative framework. This is what we call a story. Furthermore, we think that this is the natural way for people to understand things and is, therefore, the reason why story telling, joke telling, biographies, television situation comedies and fiction of all sorts are central to the human experience. We actually *do* think that putting things within a story framework is how the human mind works. Thus, this is the reason journalists like beginnings, middles and ends and is also the reason the tricks of narration — personalized accounts, pithy remarks, conflict — so appeal to us. It is not that we do not understand how science works, it is rather that we think we understand how people's brains work. (Let me note in passing that our theory of learning is not unlike Brzustowski's [2000*a, b*] presentation about how politicians reason.)

Now I would also argue that science has an almost exactly opposite epistemology. It says that you cannot truly know anything about nature, including the nature of man, until you remove it from a human story-telling framework and present it in a way that if aliens existed, they could understand not just what we know, but how we know it. This is often expressed in that most non-narrative of languages, mathematics. And when it is not mathematical, it might as well be. This is the explanation for why someone would publish an article entitled "Circularly Polarized Light Generated by Photoexcitation of Luminospheres in Glass Liquid-Crystal Films" in a recent issue of *Nature* and believe that someone would read it. I would also suggest that scientific discourse is as much about excommunication as communication. That is, the aforementioned *Nature* article uses its arcane language to advise other scientists: "if you are not really interested in this, stay away; we only want those who truly belong to be learning this."

Scientists and scientific literature go out of their way to remove the true narrative framework of discovery from the presentation of the information. You cannot find out what really went on in an interesting human fashion from a scientific paper. For those truly interested in how much the one does not capture the other, compare the book the *Double Helix* with the original *Nature* article describing the structure of DNA.

As someone with little scientific background, I further suggest that the two different ways of learning separate the presenters into two camps. Journalists do not go into journalism because they want to deal with numbers, quite the reverse. Indeed, no Canadian journalism programme I am aware of requires a statistics course for its students — something not true in the United States. And scientists do not go into science because they love to tell stories. In my experience, scientists often feel like people who would be more comfortable with an abstract of life than life itself. But as I have said: There is a rationale behind this.

Thus, we have different theories of knowledge. And, I dare say, it is not entirely clear which is better. For while science and mathematics are much better at explaining the natural world, the conveying of scientific matter in all its "scienceness" is seen by many, and perhaps most, non-scientists as somewhere between noxious and hateful. People talk often about improving the teaching of science and mathematics and thereby making them intrinsically enjoyable. I believe this is a chimera. Most people are never going to like doing quadratic equations, memorizing all the bones in the human body or working at a laboratory bench, because for them these are unnatural ways of thinking and learning.

I think that one can argue this point in a fashion scientifically; there are studies in psychology that talk about the memory power of information embedded in stories, but I would rather just argue the reality of common sense. More people read, watch and listen to the non-scientific media than they ever do scientific productions. They tell us they like truth as story telling, particularly as a story seems to be an outgrowth of experience. (As an aside, let me also point out that if one were to compare all kinds of knowledge and information-importing technologies, then clearly television with its combination of pictures, sounds and the occasional bit of written language is the most "natural" teaching medium.)

Assuming this is the case, then how do the two theories of knowledge, the media's and science's, speak to one another. The sense that what you are seeing when media and science meet is a kind of communications joke has often arisen in my mind when I see the results. My favorite fictional example comes from Douglas Adams' *Hitchhikers' Guide to the Galaxy*. There we were told that the meaning of "life, the universe and everything" is "42." This non-narrative, or "scientific" answer comes across as a big joke.

But real life can be almost as funny. I recently followed up on a story about cancer-causing aromatic amines, a chemical produced as a by-product of both frying foods and making plastics, which appeared in our paper (*The Globe and Mail*, 1998). Levels of the aromatic amines had been found in mothers' milk even when the mothers had not been exposed to them. For a journalist, the finding demanded to be broadcast because it was such a compelling narrative. The "story" said that something in our environment was poisoning our children at their mothers' breasts. Heroic Joe Blow scientist had found the venom. Now, who was to blame and how were we to eliminate the risk to — all clichés to the fore — helpless, innocent infants?

With the narrative in mind, the newspaper story told readers many scientific things about the aromatic amines. The amount of the substance, sometimes in measurements down to a few parts per billion, was presented. There was some biochemistry, the chemicals were a by-product of the digestion of seared surfaces. And there was preventative medicine. A biologist advised mothers to scrape the surface of fish and the meat to ensure that they contained as little of the aromatic amines as possible. But another question not discussed in the article was central to the issue of risk: How did the amount of aromatic amines found in the mothers' milk compare to the amount that was thought to cause cancer? I was curious and asked the reporter. "Much less," she replied, adding the scientist was not sure, maybe ten or one hundred times less. "Might it be possible that it was so much less that it was not dangerous?" I inquired. The reply was that any amount is potentially dangerous, and the scientists had told her that pregnant women should not eat the burned portions of meat and fish. Unimpressed with this explanation, I called a scientist and asked for the real numbers. He admitted he had originally told the reporter only that the numbers were very small, and only later had he checked on the exact figures. The data showed that the amount that caused cancer in mice was somewhere between 256,000 to 600,000,000 times more than he had found in the mothers' milk. I then spoke to the scientist who had counselled the mothers to scrape all their meat. "Yikes," he explained, "I didn't realize the quantity was so small"!

Let me suggest this is a story where the scientists are to blame for a clear miscommunication of risk. They did not pay any attention to the narrative thrust of their data. They did not see the scary story that their findings would "tell" nor the fear it would engender in nursing women. The journalist involved *should* have badgered the scientists to be more precise, but I understand her dilemma. She was accurately repeating what she had been told by people who should know, by experts. And she was in awe of them. Untrained in science as she was, she did not think she could challenge them. As an aside, let me say there is often amongst scientists a kind of cynicism about journalism that I have never met among my fellow reporters. We actually do want to be accurate. We are embarrassed by getting things wrong. And if the numbers contradict our stories we want to change the story.[1] But the scientist thought the journalists or their readers were not going to be interested in the numbers, so he chose not to tell them. And you know, I also think he may have been sort of interested in promoting the narrative line of "danger to nursing children" too. It sounds like something more likely to get a grant than the more truthful, "new technology finds substances in body much below dangerous levels".

Let me give you another example of how journalists and scientists miscommunicate. A story appeared in a scientific magazine describing how fidgeting caused weight loss. It was reported around the world because of its wonderful narrative — a water cooler story, as we call them, a story people tell one another. I took a second look at it, a while later. It was noted at the end of the original article that some statistics related to the research could be found at a Website. I took a look at them, I did not find any that seemed to quantify fidgeting. I called the scientists. Well, they explained, they had not been able to quantify fidgeting. What they had done is overfeed a number of people. At the end of the overfeeding, they found some people had put on a lot of weight and some not. They had put accelerometres on all their subjects and determined that those who had not put on weight had not increased their heavy exercise.

They then argued that it had to be unmeasured, non-exercising activities, things that they categorized as "fidgeting, body postures and the activities of daily life", which must account for why some individuals did not gain weight. Reporters saw the water-cooler word "fidgeting" and every story highlighted it. I asked: "Would the activities of daily life include me walking home from work?" It also included climbing stairs, shoveling a walk, gardening, working at my computer, everything but violent physical exercise. Why include fidgeting? We did not realize journalists would make such a big deal, confessed the scientists. Worse, from the point of view of miscommunication I noticed that in their measures of heavy physical activities, it turned out that the person who put on the least weight seemed to have actually decreased his activities, while the person who put on the most weight increased hers. The scientist's explanation is error in measurement technology. Maybe, but it all looked so strange, so why did not my fellow reporters not seize upon it? After all, "exercise less, keep off weight" is also a water cooler story. My explanation. The journalists read the words, they did not look at the numbers. That is, they paid attention to the explicit narrative, the words in the paper that referred to fidgeting, not to the evidence or lack of same that fidgeting was the cause of weight loss.

How does one make things better? You know, possibly, nothing will resolve these difficulties. These are two theories of knowledge that will just fight it out forever. But I want to be positive. I have long thought that there were two concrete things that could be done.

First, schooling must change. I have a most radical schooling change in mind. I think that statistics must become *the* mathematics taught in high school and university. That is to say, it is the one that everyone must be exposed to and which no one can graduate without. My reason is simple. I think that statistics is both the most narrative of the mathematical sciences, and it is the one that non-scientists need the most in their lives. One of the problems with mathematical schooling as presently constituted is that it aims to produce scientists, engineers and computer people. Interesting, but hardly socially responsible. Everyone should be exposed to narrative mathematics to understand its power and its weaknesses.

Secondly, scientists should be required to take a course in translating scientific material (with plain narrative) into English before they graduate. This can be intellectually vigorous as accurate communication can be quite tricky. My theory is that if scientists were forced to act as journalists, they would understand how their results might sound on the larger world stage. They would be forced to see that the narrative framework does matter, because if it is not there, the finding does not make much sense. Ultimately, I think scientists must be taught to communicate in the mental language of non-scientists.

Which brings me back to my initial joke. The trickiest part of the relation between science and the media is that when blind men describe an elephant they can both be somewhat right and still be all wrong.

NOTE

1. Note, there appeared during the discussion several responders who recited examples of the British press not being so ethical. My experience supports this cultural difference, and I quote the lovely doggerel rhyme stating "You cannot hope to bribe or twist the honest British journalist, but when you see what he will do, unbribed, there's no occasion to."

REFERENCES

Brzustowski, T.A. (2000*a*), "The Role of Science in Public Policy: Some Observations", in *Statistics, Science and Public Policy: The Two Cultures?* ed. A.M. Herzberg and I. Krupka, Kingston: Queen's University, pp. 107-118.

_____ (2000*b*), "Working with Canada's S&T Policy: Three Years of Learning", in *Statistics, Science and Public Policy: The Two Cultures?* ed. A.M. Herzberg and I. Krupka, Kingston: Queen's University, pp. 23-37.

The Globe and Mail (1998), "Breast Milk Found to Contain Carcinogen, Guelph Study Points to Need for Diet Change," December 18, p. A17.

PART VIII

THE UNIVERSITY CULTURE

CHAPTER 23

The Concept of the University Culture

E.B. Andersen

Is there a concept called the university culture? Or, is there one well-specified university culture? To answer this question, we must first be precise about what is a culture? C.P. Snow wrote that it is a group of people with common attitudes, common standards and patterns of behaviour, common approaches and assumptions (Snow, 1964). Given Snow's definition, there is certainly not one well-specified university culture, but in fact many. I shall try here to describe why, and to discuss where the so-called gap is to be found within the university environment, in fact, often of the same width and seriousness as when Snow wrote his book.

As for a multitude of cultures, Snow himself (1964) points out a third culture: he describes this third culture as a mixed bag (as he called it) of disciplines, including essentially what we would today describe as the social sciences, although he vaguely includes medicine and, somewhat surprisingly, architecture.

My own career as a statistician can be used effectively to describe two very different cultures within the university environment. They roughly correspond to Snow's science culture and his "third" culture. I started out as a pure mathematical statistician and worked very much in mathematical statistics for several years. Later, as is common among statisticians, I drifted slowly and steadily over into applied statistics in the social sciences. During this transformation over many years, I was able to observe those of my contemporary colleagues, who remained in the mathematical statistical environment. Unfortunately, many of the characteristics described by Snow are still valid for many scientists in departments of mathematical statistics, at least in Denmark, probably to a large extent worldwide. One aspect is that contact between the media and mathematical statisticians is extremely infrequent, if it exists at all. Mathematical statisticians seldom engage in public debates. What they are concerned about is to establish ever more sophisticated methods to understand complex structures of data by ever more sophisticated mathematics. In Denmark, we have a number of world-famous mathematical statisticians such as Ole Barndorff-Neilsen, Søren Johansen and Steffen Lauritzen. For many years now, none of them has appeared on Danish TV, or written important comments in Danish newspapers. As a result, high-level statistics is not known or understood by the general public.

As a contrast, let me describe the way some of my colleagues in the social sciences work. Here we are faced with scientists who feel that they must justify their research as being interwoven with the problems of today's society. Scientists in sociology, economics and political science as a general rule not only take their inspiration from the problems of today's society, but they are also eager to communicate their research findings to that society through television appearances or through commentaries in newspapers. They, of course, also influence public policies by serving on important government committees.

Thus, it is easy to identify at least two very different university cultures: the true scientists in the natural sciences, quite indifferent to the impact of their research on society and the social scientists, fully aware of their role as communicators of research findings relevant for society.

A final important point is the gap that can sometimes be found within one scientific discipline, even within one university department. This may even be the most profound of our problems. Let me describe two examples of such subcultures at war: in the Economics Department, of which I am now a member, there is an ongoing battle over the fundamentals of the science of economics. One group believes that mathematical economics is the true study of economics. Their aim is to find the basic principles of economic behaviour in order to establish the fundamental laws of economics. Usually it boils down to a few extremely intelligent agents working in a well-specified market, obeying certain rules of rational behaviour. The task at hand is then to discuss whether such a market and its agents can find an "equilibrium". This then is the reference point against which observed phenomena can be measured. The other group are the econometricians and the "generalists", as they are called. These economists are concerned with concrete applications of economic theories and/or statistical models that can explain, on an empirical basis, the observed oscillations of financial markets or the time series of national or regional economies. Again, the first group in this battle will only reluctantly appear on television or contribute to the ongoing debate on the government's economic policies. The second group, however, are eager to participate in public debates, in order to establish that their work is directly applicable to whatever issue is at the centre of media attention.

The next example, which is much more in the vein of C.P. Snow is the formation of a new Department of Sports Science at the University of Copenhagen. The idea was to merge the biology department with the Copenhagen School of Physical Education. The biology department constituted mainly biologists and physicians. Their rather lofty views about the seriousness and quality of their research played a significant role in later events. The School of Physical Education was primarily oriented toward practical sports training and the sociological, physiological and educational aspects of sports science. It is interesting to note that the history of sports was an area of special interest to one of the most respected scientists in the School of Physical Education. C.P. Snow identified social history as an example of what he called the "third culture".

As the process of merging the biology department and the School of Physical Education got underway, the opposing views of sports science, held by the two groups, confronted each other. The biologists and physicians (with few exceptions) were unable to accept the people from the School of Physical Education as equally worthy and respectable scientists. At the heart of this was in effect C.P. Snow's concern, namely whether pure scientists or those who, justifiably or not, consider themselves to be pure scientists, could accept and communicate with serious researchers from the more applied sciences.

I am unable to describe what a university culture is. And even more distressing, I am unable to make a list of university cultures identifiable by their characteristics, and decide which fields of science belong where. But maybe this is not the most important thing. As the battle between the areas of economics showed, the real problem is to build bridges in the sense that scientists from different science cultures accept each other and join in research that crosses borders. New and often surprising results occur.

Unfortunately, we are not there yet, not by many, many miles.

REFERENCE

Snow, C.P. (1964), *The Two Cultures and the Scientific Revolution*, Cambridge: Cambridge University Press.

CHAPTER 24

Cultural Shifts: Humanities to Science to Computation

R.W. Oldford

SHIFT IN CULTURE

In 1959, C.P. Snow was writing at a time when the "scientific culture" was ascendant and enjoying great popularity. The twentieth century was a new age of enlightenment likened to that of the Elizabethan, with Rutherford as Shakespeare.

Although the twentieth century, and particularly the times between and after the two world wars, had been very good to science, it was not so good to the letters. George Orwell wrote "The literature of liberalism is coming to an end. As for the writer, he is . . . merely an anachronism, a hangover from the Bourgeois age, . . . from now onwards the all important fact for the creative writer is going to be that this is not a writer's world" (de la Mothe, 1992, p. 34). Overstated perhaps, but it does convey the widely held sentiment that it was a better time to start a scientific career than a literary one.[1]

For the most part, Snow's essay on the "Two Cultures" was directed at the "other culture" — the older, established culture of the literary intellectual. Just look at the tests he applies. It is hard to imagine, even now, that any native English-speaking scientist could have made it through secondary school without having read at least one Shakespearean play (and Shaw, and Ibsen, and Chekhov, etc.); but it is still debatable whether a non-scientist should know the second law of thermodynamics (at least as *The Second Law of Thermodynamics*). A somewhat comparable literary challenge might be having read and appreciated Horace or Cicero.

Perhaps the most telling sign of this one-sidedness is that scientists, for the most part, seem to agree with Snow's assessment while humanists have been quite dismissive of his "superficial" and even "silly" dichotomy.[2] Snow's scientific culture, feeling its youthful strength and insecurity, wants recognition from the established "intellectuals". To me, this seems to be more symptomatic of a shift than of a separation.

In his rebuttal to critics, written four years after the Rede Lecture, Snow struggled to defend his choice of the word "culture" and of the number "two". Parenthetically he remarks that "No one, I think, has yet complained about the definite article".

The choice of "culture" is defended by appealing to a dictionary definition meaning "intellectual development, development of the mind" and also to the anthropological distinction made between living groups of people. Were he to adopt a definition from Coleridge of culture being those "qualities and faculties which characterize our humanity", Snow admits that neither the literary nor the scientific constitute cultures but rather subcultures. In this light, the cultural shift is one of emphasis. In Snow's view, too long has our culture nurtured the literary and starved the scientific. He is interested in having the balance redressed.

Accepting Snow's choice of the word culture, it is easy to see that the number two could be many more. Every specialization could be called a culture. Indeed, in the forty years that have passed since the Rede Lecture, sufficient has been written on Snow's "Two Cultures" that it might legitimately constitute a specialization of its own, a humbling thought for those of us who have been asked to address the matter for the first time.

Snow defends the number "two" on grounds of simplicity; it crystallizes the two extremes for contrast. It is interesting that he briefly considers three by the possible separation of technology from science. He dismisses it because he has observed that the technologist, when designing a new technology, goes through much the same experience as a scientist in designing an experiment. To this I feel compelled to add the words of the professional chemist, Primo Levi, whose fame is established as a writer. They should evoke kindred feelings from any theoretician:

> I now felt in the writing a complex, intense, and new pleasure, similar to that I felt as a student when penetrating the solemn order of differential calculus. It was exalting to search and find, or create, the right word, that

is, commensurate, concise, and strong; to dredge up events from my memory and describe them with the greatest rigour and the least clutter (Levi, 1975, p. 160).

A more understandable justification would be that technology has so long been tied up with science that its separation seems unnatural to Snow.

One thing that the number two has resulted in is an entire cottage industry devoted to finding number three. Snow himself started this. Although "technology" was rejected, in his rebuttal to his critics he did introduce what he saw to be the beginnings of a third culture. This third culture was being formed by the social sciences, in Snow's words those

> intellectual persons in a variety of fields — social history, sociology, demography, political science, economics, government (in the American sense), psychology, medicine, and social arts such as architecture.... All of them are concerned with how human beings are living or have lived — and concerned, not in terms of legend, but of fact (Snow, 1964, p. 70).

Allan Bloom, in his book *The Closing of the American Mind*, identifies the big three disciplines which "rule the academic roost and determine what is knowledge" (Bloom, 1987, p. 356). These are the natural sciences, which are doing well, the social sciences which are more robust being more in harmony with the natural sciences, although in Bloom's opinion they only succeed in "aping ... the methods of natural science" (ibid., p. 358), and the humanities which are languishing, having decided "to proudly set up shop next door" rather than to "humbly find a place at [the] court" (ibid.) of natural science. The shift from Snow's view of the cultural problems to Bloom's is staggering.

Snow thought that when this third culture came into existence it would serve to ease communication between the two cultures. This was because this third culture would have to "be on speaking terms with the scientific one ... just to do its job". Perhaps it has but, if Bloom is correct, the communication sadly ended there.

More recently, John Brockman and others have seized on the communication between science and other cultures as the hallmark of the third culture. His third culture consists of scientific thinkers who are able to communicate directly with the lay public. These include well-known scientists like Richard Dawkins, Stephen Jay Gould and Roger Penrose, and well-known computer scientists like Daniel Hillis and Marvin Minsky.

The primary medium for discourse seems to be the Internet where articles and follow-up commentary are posted to open discussion groups.[3] Whereas early scientists, at least as early as Archimedes, exchanged their ideas in letters written to other scientists, challenging them to think, this third culture purports to replicate the exchange but with a much larger collection of thinkers (scientists and the layperson alike). Writers and commentators are the third culture, a culture of individuals whose ideas are reviewed by the public rather than by a more traditional (and likely more conservative) peer system. Brockman writes: "Unlike previous intellectual pursuits, the achievements of the third culture are not the marginal disputes of a quarrelsome mandarin class: They will affect the lives of everybody on the planet" (Brockman, 1999, p. 2). Heady stuff. Absent the Internet, and so the immediacy of discussion, and this is just a group of scientists, albeit articulate ones, trying to communicate to the lay public. Nothing new to that.

In fact, Snow had been quick in his rebuttal to point out the existence of such writers as J. Bronowski, G.H. Hardy and A.N. Whitehead who in "some of the most beautiful prose of our time" (1964, p. 63) wrote directly for public consumption. But this is not a third culture in Snow's view, simply additional evidence that science is deserving of the word culture.

Scientists, curiously, have often not been kind to other scientists who write for the lay public, particularly if it is found to be promoting a pet theory. An early example is Descartes's biting review of Galileo's famous book, the *Two New Sciences*: "fashion of writing in dialogues, where he introduces three persons who do nothing but exalt each of his inventions in turn, greatly assists in [over]pricing his merchandise. (In a letter to the great experimental scientist Marin Mersenne [1588-1647], dated October 11, 1638.)" (Drake, 1975, p. 388). One is reminded of the current and much more public disagreement between Gould and Dawkins where one worries publicly that the other writes perhaps too well.

A more interesting, and to me much more plausible, candidate for a third culture is the one rejected by Snow, namely, technology. Not technology as Snow understood it in 1963. Far too much has changed since. And not that of the specialized technology expressly designed to address scientific questions. The critical technology here is the general purpose computer which now appears in schools and homes throughout every industrial society. The ubiquity of this extremely malleable technology together with the instantaneous worldwide communication between its users has enabled the growth of what Kevin Kelly, the executive editor of *Wired* magazine, has called the "nerd culture".

Kelly (1998) coined the term in an essay in *Science*. There he described the nerd culture as an outgrowth of science, but one that is quite separate from Snow's two cultures:

> The nerd culture pursues neither understanding of the natural world nor of the human condition; it pursues novelty.
> Questions are framed so that the answer is a new technology.
> It creates possibilities.
> Creation is preferred to creativity.

According to Kelly: "The culture of science, so long in the shadow of the culture of art, now has another orientation to contend with, one grown from its own rib" (1998, p. 993). If Kelly is right, our culture is shifting in an important way again. This time in a direction that might affect science more than the humanities.

THE STUDENT

Imagine a student now entering university. The nerd culture is part of the culture. It could not be otherwise. What does this student expect of a university education? What do we expect of this student?

It is a time-honoured tradition in academe to lament that students are not what they once were. But this just is not true in any important way. In terms of intelligence and motivation little has changed since ancient Greece.

Students have always enjoyed, and will always enjoy, the contemplative and the puzzling. And they have always been, and will always be, interested in personal gain: whether financial, an affiliation with an elite, fame, or power for its own sake. It is no accident, for example, that students appearing in the Platonic dialogues are intent on honing their rhetorical and dialectical skills so as to acquire and wield political power. Nor is it a coincidence that the elite of Athenian society would charge Socrates not just with impiety but also with the corruption of their youth. One can imagine the appeal of a classical education to a youth in classical times.

Our principal means of giving meaningful power to students is through specialization. Acquiring some mastery of a subject requires spending considerable time immersed in it, exploring a terrain so well that it not only becomes familiar, but one can at least imagine how it might be extended into new territory. This is an intellectual power that every educated person should experience. Even so, a specialization that cannot assure the student a certain success in society after graduation will be avoided, if not shunned.

Natural science might still provide that path to success but the nerd culture has already informed students that computer science delivers in spades! It is fresh, exciting, important and modern — and has yet to experience its Chernobyl.

Like earlier times in the natural sciences, the nerd culture presents an encouraging and friendly face. Internet newsgroups and the like provide a supportive and competitive forum for neophytes and experts alike. Recall nineteenth-century science, when letters to *Nature* might recount the strange behaviour of a gentleman's dog, or describe flora and fauna observed on a trip abroad.

Start-up costs are minimal. One achieves 0 to 60 per cent effectiveness in real world application remarkably fast. Many budding computer science students make money with these skills before reaching university — graduate specialization is unnecessary. Think of the feedback to the student: older generations are amazed and the skills transfer easily to almost any area of application!

Intellectually, general purpose computers are machines that manipulate symbols — some of these just happen to represent floating point numbers. The technology is extremely malleable and so provides a new medium for representing ideas, expressing relationships, and modelling just about anything. The only bounds are the imagination and the finite but very large number of states.

This is power — power with some immediacy. Joseph Weizenbaum expressed it first, and best, as follows:

> The computer programmer, however, is a creator of universes for which he alone is the lawgiver. So, of course, is the designer of any game. But universes of virtually unlimited complexity can be created in the form of computer programs. Moreover, and this is a crucial point, systems so formulated and elaborated act out their programmed scripts. They compliantly obey their laws and vividly exhibit their obedient behaviour. No playwright, no stage director, no emperor, however powerful, has ever exercised such absolute authority to arrange a stage or a field of battle and to command such unswervingly dutiful actors or troops (Weizenbaum, 1976, p. 115).

That this power corrupts was Weizenbaum's point, applied to the often over-reaching claims of artificial intelligence.

CHALLENGES

The nerd culture is, I think, a genuine cultural shift. Perhaps not as large as that from a humanities-dominated culture to a science-dominated culture, but it does seem more a shift than a fashion. How we are to accommodate this shift is a significant challenge to the university and to the natural sciences.

The last shift, heralded by C.P. Snow's Rede Lecture, was accommodated at a substantial cost to the humanities — a cost from which we have yet to recover. Standing proudly aloof, as Bloom said of the humanities, seems a strategy intent on reducing one's influence. And aping the methods of the foreign culture is quickly seen for what it is.

Fortunately, there is much in the sciences that is already heavily computational which could easily be, and should be, made more visible to the student. Gratuitous computational use, however, is not on; aping is aping. In this it is important to remember that, while we may regard the computer as a powerful and even essential tool, in the nerd culture it is the *raison d'être,* a malleable medium for expression — in, of and for itself.

The challenges to the natural sciences are: to ensure that science and scientific reasoning are an important part of everyone's education, to attract the good students to the sciences, and to apply scientific knowledge and reasoning to this new specialization.

The broader challenge to the university culture is to incorporate important cultural shifts without sacrificing the best of what went before. We have a new shift that requires addressing and we have yet to deal justly with the last much larger shift.

The same questions still need to be answered. Northrop Frye argued in 1963 that C.P. Snow's problem of two (or now more) cultures is not a major problem of society.

It is not the humanist's ignorance of science or the scientist's ignorance of the humanities which is important, but their common ignorance of the society they are living in, and their responsibilities as citizens. It is not the humanist's inability to read a textbook in physics or the physicist's ability to read a textbook in literary criticism, but the inability of both of them to read the morning paper with a kind of insight demanded of educated citizens. (From *The Changing Pace in Canadian Education*, the Kenneth E. Norris Memorial Lecture delivered at Sir George Williams University, January 24, 1963 as reprinted in Frye, 1988, p. 69).

What should constitute an education? Must specializations be so specialized? And so soon? Bloom (1987) suggests that posing some of these questions would be a threat to the peace, yet pose them we must. But where?

This series of conferences is important in that they provide a rare forum where scholars from across the spectrum of intellectual inquiry can raise and discuss these and like questions. How to foster the same kind of discussion back at our home institutions is a challenge for all of us.

NOTES

1.   This case is convincingly made by de la Mothe.
2.   For example, Allan Bloom, Russell Kirk, F.R. Leavis and Northrop Frye.
3.   The principal Website is www.edge.org/3rd_culture.

REFERENCES

Bloom, A. (1987), *The Closing of the American Mind: How Higher Education Has Failed Democracy and Impoverished the Souls of Today's Students*, New York: Simon & Schuster.

Brockman, J. (1999), "The Third Culture", (<http://www.edge.org/3rd-culture/3rd-continue.html>).

de la Mothe, J. (1992), *C.P. Snow and the Struggle of Modernity*, Austin: University of Texas Press.

Drake, S. (1978), *Galileo at Work: His Scientific Biography*, New York: Dover Publications, Inc.

Frye, N. (1988), *On Education*, Markham, Ont.: Fitzhenry and Whiteside.

Kelly, K. (1998), "The Third Culture", *Science* 279:992-993.

Levi, P. (1975), *The Periodic Table,* (1984 translation by R. Rosenthal) Everyman's Library, Toronto: Alfred A. Knopf.

Snow, C.P. (1964), *The Two Cultures and the Scientific Revolution*, Cambridge: Cambridge University Press.

Weizenbaum, J. (1976), *Computer Power and Human Reason: From Judgment to Calculation*, San Francisco: W.H. Freeman and Co.

PART IX

THE ROLE OF THE SCIENTISTS

CHAPTER 25

What of the Role of the Scientists?

P. Campbell

I shall focus on two problems and celebrate one other aspect of the topic of the role of the scientist in the two cultures. The problems are to do with money and society. The celebration is of science itself, but expressed in a way I hope you will find stimulating. The context of all this is that multivalent little word "culture".

Let me start with a millennial thought. Think of the difference in one art form and one branch of science between 1899 and 1919. Between these dates, composers demolished traditional tenets of musical structure and expression. Stravinsky moved from the world of Rimsky Korsakov and Skryabin to that of the Rite of Spring. Schoenberg moved from the post-Wagnerian world to that of wholehearted atonality. In both cases, these giants, who were to influence most of the classical music of the century, moved instinctively in a visionary way and with a total lack of compromise.

A similar process happened in physics. From an era of mistaken certainty that all the rest was detail, Einstein and Bohr pursued their visions of what nature might be like and discovered new principles, at odds with everyday experience, which underlay new ways of describing nature: quantum mechanics and relativity. Physicists and chemists, at least, have been pursuing the implications of those principles ever since, while biology has been revolutionized thanks to techniques thereby made possible.

The links between these developments in music and physics are non-existent. But in terms of roles, in terms of a cultural impact, they are very similar. In representing ideals of progress within their respective disciplines or professions, the people I have mentioned have been iconic for similar reasons: thinking hard and deeply for the sake of it, facing up to their opponents, and being utterly uncompromising in the intellectual and instinctive pursuit of their goals.

In a 1998 BBC poll, the British public named Darwin and Einstein as two millennial figures in their history. As with the figures mentioned earlier, that status has ultimately nothing to do with personality and everything to do with the depth and breadth of their impact. But it is also, indirectly, to do with their irrepressibly exploratory professional characters. Darwin, having shaken the world with his work on the origin of the species, spent the last years of his life examining the behaviour of earthworms. Einstein pursued a goal that still challenges today's theoretical physicists: unified explanations of the fundamental forces of nature.

But it would be worrying if the iconic role of the scientist could only be discussed with reference to these giants. Thus, I would like to celebrate very briefly two contemporary scientists whom I know, but whom the public does not. One is a Cambridge palaeontologist, Nick Shackleton. He is an experimentalist who spends most of his time categorizing the shells of dead sea organisms called foraminifera, through painstaking analysis of such shells in their sedimentary contexts. Through analyses of the isotopes of oxygen and carbon, he has been able to trace the history of temperature and carbon dioxide content through tens of thousands of years, spanning the last ice age. His work is characterized by a careful objectivity in probing what he is working with coupled with the great scope of what it could reveal. I have seen how, at conferences, his capacity to go that little bit deeper into the conclusions he pursues and elucidates inspires colleagues of both his and the younger generations.

The second person is the theoretical physicist Michael Berry at Bristol. Waves are his intellectual passion. But think what an enormous range that opens up to him as a mathematical physicist: from the ocean tides to the regular and irregular motions of celestial bodies, to nonlinear dynamics and chaos, to atmospheric optics, and to the wave-representation of matter that underlies our understanding of the behaviour of atoms. The seeking after, or at least pleasure in, underlying unification is characteristic of the scientist, alongside the pursuit of the implications of ideas about what the underlying "truth" is. Like Shackleton, the depth as well as the breadth of his thinking inspires other physicists and, indeed, mathematicians.

The discovery of the genetic code in the 1950s opened up precisely that sort of unifying insight into all organisms. I am not sure that Watson's book (1968), *The Double Helix*, really does justice to the character of their discovery. Can it be that Crick and Watson were just very clever? Is there, culturally speaking, more than that to be celebrated about them? But do they have to die, first?

So far I have tried to highlight that iconic aspect of science, which is surely where its impact on culture stands alongside that of the arts. But now let me consider, somewhat in contrast, two other aspects of science, both rooted in science as it is today, and both with cultural implications.

First, there is money. Not funding, but patents, industrial consultancy and entrepreneurialism. I am not only talking about companies whose specific role is to develop technology and profit by it. I am also talking about scientists in academia. In biology especially, the difference between science and technology is getting smaller and smaller. Gene sequences can be patented.

In a little-quoted section of his Rede Lecture, C.P. Snow (1959) attacked academic and cultural attitudes to business and to engineering in the United Kingdom. That has completely changed as far as business is concerned. We live in enterprise cultures — in North America, certainly in the United Kingdom and increasingly, though much more sluggishly, in continental Europe. If the measures are profits, we know that gene-manipulative biotech has a long way to go, but other parts of biology and the physics and chemistry bases have spawned many valuable companies. If the cultural measure is money invested, venture capital or personal wealth gained, these post-scientific contributions are vibrant. If the cultural measure is coverage in books and in the media, then high-tech entrepreneurism does very well in the United States, poorly in the United Kingdom and abysmally in continental Europe. There are many reasons for this.

However positive a role this aspect of science may represent, there is a double edge to it. Conflicts of interest abound, potentially and in practice. It is clear, for example, on the west coast of the United States, that too many excellent scientists are torn between their obligations to their students and those to their stockholders.

There is also a threat to another role of the scientist, which is my third emphasis: engaging with society, whether in the media or in advice to the government. Conflicts of interest, through financial or contractual engagement, are making that disinterested adviser harder and harder to find. In the field of nuclear waste in the United Kingdom, it was all but impossible to find a geologist not tied in with the green parties or the nuclear industry. The government was recently forced to restructure their biotechnology advisory committees so as to remove members with conflicts of interest.

To look at relationships with society, it is worth starting with trust. The public's trust in scientists varies in many ways. Einstein would be trusted, but would the public trust today's scientists who are involved in any way in bioscience? Biovision '99 was a conference in Lyons earlier in 1999 for those involved in biotechnology in Europe. It included sessions on public perceptions, including guest speakers from the United States, as well as demonstrations by Greenpeace. The talks highlighted the contrast between the United States and Europe. In the United States, belief in science is strong, trust in technology strong, the voice of the bio-industry is strong (though not necessarily trusted) and the voice of the green movement relatively weak. The contrast, in all respects, with Europe is very marked, especially the low profile of industry spokespersons in the middle of controversies. Surveys suggest that scientists in Europe are trusted rather than distrusted, thankfully, but not as trusted as they should be.

Then there was the United Kingdom public consultation. I should declare an interest: I was a member of the government's advisory panel for this initiative. This was a highly democratic exercise, allowing public participation in a government reshaping of the United Kingdom's regulatory system for bioscience and biotechnology. An independent body — the MORI polling organization — conducted six two-day workshops throughout the country followed by a nationwide quantitative survey questioning eleven thousand people.

On the first day of each of the workshops, twenty participants aired their views about their understanding of such issues as xenotransplantation, (GM), crops and cloning. They were then given a briefing on key aspects of the science, current debates and current regulatory processes. On the second day they were given the chance, in effect, to design their own regulatory system, including recommendations about representation of various interest groups, and the supply of information to the public. The results are still preliminary and confidential.[1] But it confirms others' findings that in this area, scientists are much less trusted than environmentalists, though more trusted by a long way than industry and the media. It also demonstrates something that I think is culturally very significant: the public across the spectrum loved to come and talk about these issues. Not so much about science itself, but about its consequences on their lives and environment. Of course, we know that the public is fascinated by the results of science, but are starved of basic and reliable information when they need it. In my view, governments can and must do much more in providing information, such as on the Internet.

Here is a different problem of two cultures: acute scepticism and concern side by side with acute fascination — in Europe, at least. Does this mean that Europe's scientific culture is more or less mature than that of the United States?

I started with a millennial state of the 1900s. The scientific state of 2000 is not dissimilar, as seen at the turn of the century: lots of details to be worked out on all fronts, and, in fundamental physics, a clear agenda of looking ever deeper. The coming century will, of course, confront us or our descendants with the limits of what science can say about the mind, and that will surely have a cultural impact, as may the discovery of planets similar to the Earth orbiting other stars. But let us also hope that by 2010, something astonishing has emerged that will upset all expectations of our understanding of the way the physical or biological world works: that sort of discovery is the greatest privilege a scientist can yearn for.

And to finish on a cultural note, I can do no better than quote *Nature*, a review of a biography of another relatively unsung hero of twentieth century science, the theoretical physicist John Archibald Wheeler.

"What is theoretical physics for Wheeler? It is a search to unify experience and at the same time to prosecute aesthetic concerns" (Galison, 1999).

NOTE

1. A report has subsequently been published and can be found on the UK Office of Science and Technology's Website at http://www.dti.gov.uk/ost/ostbusiness/index.htm.

REFERENCES

Galison, P. (1999), a review of Wheeler's "Geons, Black Holes and Quantum Foam: A Life in Physics", *Nature* 398:677.

Snow, C.P. (1959), "The Two Cultures", *Encounter* 12:17-24.

Watson, J.D. (1968), *The Double Helix: A Personal Account of the Discovery of the Structure of DNA*, London: Weidenfeld & Nicholson.

CHAPTER 26

Public Understanding of Science

L. Wolpert

We no longer believe that if only the public knew more science, everything would be all right: it is important to appreciate what public concerns really are. One of the many problems in dealing with this area is: What does one want the public to actually know about science? It is also important to realize that there are many publics, from the politicians to the general newspaper reading public, from *The Express* to *The Times*. I do not, I regret, have a clear answer.

In other words, if the good fairy comes to you and says, "I'll instruct the public tomorrow in some aspect of science, would you want them to know the second law of thermodynamics or the genetic code?" I would like them to know that science is the best way to understand how the world works and why it *is* the best. I would like them to know something about the process of science and the importance of evidence as distinct from anecdote. It is how one actually assesses evidence. If I had to choose a particular example I would like them to comprehend clinical trials. If a doctor says to a patient, "The journals say that this treatment does not work but in my experience...." Flee from that doctor instantly. Only trust evidence-based medicine. I would also like the public to realize that science is based on peer review and consensus.

With regard to communication with the general public, I will briefly describe some of the things the Committee for the Public Understanding of Science (COPUS), a joint organization of the Royal Society, British Association for the Advancement of Science and the Royal Institution, has tried to do. One of the areas to which it has given a great deal of attention is that of training scientists, or having training courses available for scientists, to deal with the media: how to present information, how to be interviewed and to understand how the media works. They, along with the British Association, have an interesting programme called Media Fellowships. Young scientists can apply to work in some aspect of the media for three months. They are paid to work in newspapers such as the *Daily Express*, in BBC News and at ITV television. They get a real feeling of what it is like to work with journalists and people in the media. It has been a very successful programme. COPUS also organizes workshops, one of these brings scientists together with journalists to better understand their different aims. The annual British Association Conference hosts a major session in which all the people involved in the public's understanding of science come together and exchange experiences as to how they think they can best proceed. I think one of the virtues of COPUS is that on occasion it can exert a great deal of influence on bodies like the BBC.

One of the difficult problems in the public's understanding of science is evaluating success. There is the illusion that if things change, then this is success, but evaluating the public's understanding of science is difficult. I do not think anyone has found a very satisfactory way of doing this. One of the things that COPUS ought to be doing is keeping an audit: keeping a record of how things are changing, whatever the causes. I would like to know how many reviews of scientific books are there in the media and how has this changed over time? How has reporting of science in the papers changed over time? There are, fortunately, a number of people who are doing some of this. They are keeping and evaluating records. It is curious that those of us who are involved in the communication of science do not use science to actually try and understand the process. We rely too heavily on anecdote and yet attack anecdote when it comes into other areas. I have yet to meet someone in the public understanding of science who does not know how to *do* public understanding of science. It is rather like doctors or people in medical schools. No one who is on a selection committee for medical students admits to not knowing how to select the best medical students regardless of the fact that they have zero evidence as to whether they are doing it well. We really need some better way of understanding and evaluating what we are actually doing.

One is caught in a dilemma with the public understanding of science as to whether one is doing public relations or not. I always say that we are not in the public relations "game" and as I say it I know I am lying slightly. I take the view that scientists involved in the public understanding of science are not involved in public relations. However, there is some evidence that the more the public understands about science, the more hostile they may become; for example, the incidences of genetically modified foods, the more Monsanto explained to people what it was about, the more hostile people became. I think it would be a great mistake for scientists to become involved in public relations. If it really turns out that when the public really understand what science is about they are against it, we may have to accept this.

What I cling to in relation to the public understanding of science is access. What I mean by this is that scientists should ensure that those members of the public who want access to science should have it through the print media, television, museums or science centres. The chance to have easy access to science is important and in Britain on the whole, it is fairly good. There are, for example, many science centres throughout this country, and I think that this has led to a strong interest in science.

I am going to end with an example of one of the most important things in the public understanding of science that has happened in recent years and it relates to the Swiss referendum on genetically modified organisms. In late 1998, in Switzerland, there was a referendum in which a proposition was put forward that there should be no transgenic animals or plants made in Switzerland. If this referendum were passed it would mean that no one in Switzerland could genetically modify organisms in any way whatsoever. A great deal of fundamental biological research particularly in medical research, involves genetic modification. For one of my colleagues in Geneva, a Professor of Genetics, it would have meant that if this law were passed he would not be able to continue with this work and would have to leave Switzerland.

For six to nine months before the actual vote, it looked as if the referendum was going to pass: around 70 per cent of the Swiss public wanted to ban genetically modified organisms. The scientific community then began to organize themselves. The final vote was 70 per cent against the proposal. The explanation lies partly in natural Swiss conservativism, they really do not like changing things too quickly. They also recognized that biotechnology companies would leave Switzerland and this would not be a good thing financially. But one of the most important things was the realization that the public needed to trust the scientists. This was achieved by direct contact between scientists and the general public. The audiences saw a person, someone they might recognize. This contact is essential to public understanding.

PART X

FINAL COMMENTS

CHAPTER 27

Crumbs from a Low Table

Sir David Cox

I want to remark on several points that we have discussed. First, we spent some time on the funding of science in Canada. This was interesting. From the point of view of the mathematical sciences, I know that many of us in the United Kingdom have always admired the Natural Sciences and Engineering Research Council of Canada system for the way it supports younger people without a lot of bureaucracy. It would have been good to have seen something like that in the United Kingdom, but so far as I can see that kind of support is counter to most government policies over recent years.

Secondly, there have been signs of tension between the physical and biological sciences. I had naïvely assumed that not only had an armistice been declared many years ago, but a peace treaty signed. It would be a pity if that was the Treaty of Versailles and that we are about to see more tension between the two sides; this seems quite unjustified. There is, however, some tension within the biological sciences about the proportion of support due for genetics. Everyone admires the beauties of modern genetics, but my impression among some medical people, for example, is that they are unclear what public health impacts there are going to be and that these may turn out to be in the end much less than is sometimes claimed. This implies that support of more classical lines of enquiry, for example, of standard epidemiological studies, is still very important.

Thirdly, there has been much criticism of social science. It is worth stressing that an important body of work in social science consists of careful empirical study, not marred by overtheorizing. For example, at Nuffield College, Oxford there has been published a number of books on election studies, one on the referendum recently held about devolution in Scotland and Wales. These books are careful collections of data, appropriate analysis of quite searching questions, not merely of how people vote but about their attitudes and expectations. This does not contribute to some vast body of knowledge of theory about the nature of nationalism or about any of the other "isms" on which some political theorists are so keen. But they are a solid addition to understanding. Whether they are science or not is a matter of terminology, but I think we should recognize their value.

Fourthly, there was some discussion near the beginning of whether it would be a good idea if more government ministers were scientists. Of course, in the United Kingdom, the shadow of Mrs. Thatcher hovers threateningly over that question! Perhaps no more need be said. It seems to me more important that Ministers are open-minded about issues, and have some appreciation of uncertainty, especially of its effect on decision-making.

As well, we discussed briefly the advisory role of scientists, both in industry and in government. That academics should be involved in the non-academic world to some extent is undoubtedly excellent, and of course, in statistics this has been going on for many years. That they should become deeply involved, however, without giving up their university duties alarms me. For example, I do not see how someone can be the head of a large academic university department and at the same time in effect be running a private business. This must in the long run be harmful to all sides from a number of points of view. Somewhat connected with this is the role of scientists in legal cases. This may be particularly awkward in highly confrontational systems. The book *A Civil Action* (Harr, 1995) describes in great detail a case in Massachusetts where water pollution may have led to a cluster of cases of leukemia. I was left with the sense that this was an odd way of trying to settle factual issues. Did or did not the pollution from these two chemical companies induce a cluster of cases? The answer may be difficult to find and uncertain, but the confrontational way of getting at it seems unfortunate.

The role of newspapers, television and the media was also discussed. By and large it seems to me that the work that appears in the more serious British national newspapers on science is of a high standard and I admire the ability to be able to write about a wide range of topics at relatively short notice and with considerable lucidity. The occasional error is not surprising! What I do find alarming, however, is the use of this sort of journalism to press controversial issues. One example is the theory that HIV is not the cause for AIDS. It is entirely right and proper that it should be widely known that there are a few scientists who believe that the causal route is different, but that the newspapers should be used to press such a view strongly and argue for the associated policy decisions is alarming.

Finally, we discussed accountability, although not quite in the form that I expected, which was that we would deal with public accountability of universities and research institutes, discussing research assessment exercises, teaching assessment exercises, league tables and so forth. Here the question is not whether we have such accountability and exercises, but how to achieve them without either a vast bureaucratic process, time wasting and quality lowering, or the setting up of criteria that lead to playing silly games and second-guessing the rules. An extreme case was a report of a colleague who had been advised by his Vice-Chancellor "not to do this research; it is shared with another University and you will only get half the credit in the research assessment exercise"! Now this is corrupt, but moreover the rules may change, so that it is entirely possible that the next time collaboration between universities will get very strong encouragement. Playing to the short-term rules is self-defeating, and in any case extremely harmful in leading to short-term views on crucial issues and new appointments.

REFERENCE

Harr, J. (1995), *A Civil Action*, New York: Vintage.

CHAPTER 28

Concluding Ruminations

J. Meisel

The curse of contributing to a concluding session or chapter like this is that virtually all pertinent ideas and facts have already been presented by others, probably better than one can do it oneself; the blessing is that the title "Discussion" provides a *carte blanche* permitting the introduction of any subject under the sun. Ideally, of course, one ought deftly to summarize the principal foregoing arguments and identify the gems of thought glistening in one's memory, but this is a task quite beyond my talents, even if it could be done in the limited time available.

Instead, I propose to make some random comments arising from my ruminations about what has come before and suggest a couple of possible paths for the future.

But before dipping into this tutti-frutti bowl, I wish to be solemn for a while and refer to Gerhard Herzberg, one of the principal Godfathers of the Herstmonceux conferences on Statistics, Science and Public Policy. As David McLay observed, in some highly apposite comments, he died on March 3, 1999. There are many here better qualified than I to attest to his piercing brilliance as a scientist and science statesman. Although, through the Royal Society of Canada, of which he had been President for a term, I had numerous encounters with him that could be termed quasi-scientific, our paths crossed more often in relation to his exemplary civic involvement. Gerhard was active in, and lent his name to, a very large number of causes promoting peace, international understanding and social and civic responsibility. There were no two cultures here, not just science and music which were his passions, but also amelioration of the human condition generally. C.P. Snow must have approved.

A fellow bleeding heart, I had occasion, from time to time, to be allied with him in support of various causes we thought worthwhile. In this sphere, too, he was a model providing inspiring leadership to others.

Partly, of course, because of his close relationship with his daughter, but also, I am pretty sure, because he liked the idea, he was a stalwart and creative supporter of the Herstmonceux conferences. He provided ideas, suggestions and encouragement, although his fragile health prevented him from attending; but there is no doubt that he was with us in spirit — before, during and after the gatherings. Agnes made sure of that.

Among the many thought provoking comments presented to this conference, none surpass the stimulating, indeed, scintillating address by Professor Lewis Wolpert. Nevertheless, I found his view of Snow a bit too severe. We cannot dismiss Sir Charles lightly, since in his person there is a fortuitous convergence of several factors, almost defining the history of science during his lifetime: the historical development of the Western world, particularly in relation to the industrial revolution; the *Zeitgeist*; Snow's own experiences in science; Cambridge; government; and his vocation as writer. These produced insights and sensitivity which evoked a sympathetic and grateful resonance in many eyes and ears.

Indeed, one assertion of Professor Wolpert's eloquently supports the Rede Lecture thesis of there being two cultures — the scientific and the literary. Science, Professor Wolpert told us, "is the best way to understand how the world works" (Wolpert, 2000, p. 223). Surely, the dictum only applies to *some* phenomena, notably the natural world. Events in the Balkans or Ireland, Muslim fundamentalism, Beethoven's late quartets, the appeal of Monet's water garden near Giverny; these and many other phenomena defy explanation by the scientific culture unless the latter is given an impossibly broad definition. Now Professor Wolpert, of all people, is perfectly aware of this. That he could let slip the statement just quoted suggests that there *are* two cultures and that even the most catholic and eclectic spirits risk entrapment by the exclusivist tendencies of one or the other of them. Although, as I noted earlier, C.P. Snow worried primarily about the failings of literary culture in comprehending and complementing science culture, there are faults on both sides: sometimes each makes claims for itself that only both can live up to by complementing their respective visions.

One rumination inevitably bubbles up toward the conclusion of a conference: Did it achieve its goal? How good was it? In the present case, excellent contributions, for the most part, increased our understanding and compelled us to think anew of old problems or to do so in a fresh way, at variance with our customary stance. Fascinating data were introduced, references to numerous articles and books reminded us that we are not as well read as we would like to be, and pointed us in the right direction. We were stimulated and informed. Bravo !

But there were also some deficiencies. Two, in particular, require notice, because by identifying them, we may do better in the future. They are (i) a certain insularity and (ii) discontinuity in relation to previous sessions.

First, possibly because of the very British qualities of C.P. Snow, and the weighty presence of so many Canadians, the intellectual context of the discourse was essentially North Atlantic. A few leaves of learning blew in from elsewhere, but the major thrust of the topics discussed, experiences invoked, and cases examined centred around the North Atlantic communities. An index of these items would, I expect, contain numerous entries from the United States, the United Kingdom and Canada (with the occasional nod in the direction of Scandinavia) but there would be a striking paucity of matter originating in France, Germany, Italy or Spain or Eastern Europe. This reflects not only the origins of the participants but also the confines of their intellectual and professional horizons.

Secondly, every gathering in the present series met to ponder the topic of "Statistics, Science, and Public Policy" (SSPP — as the stylish logo of the conferences reminds us). In all cases but the first one the sessions were linked to a particular perspective: hazards and risks; science and the public trust; and in the present case, the two cultures. The common focus of SSPP leads one to expect the building up of some cumulative knowledge and insights, to which reference would occasionally be made and from which further arguments would be developed. This could be expected particularly since the proceedings of previous sessions are available to the participants, even greenhorns treading this path for the first time. But most of the authors and speakers tend to depart from a *tabula rasa* hell-bent on yet again inventing the wheel. This may be a bit too harsh a reading but it is not entirely off the mark. It might be wise to suggest to participants in future sessions, if any, that a perusal of the record of previous conferences makes a useful launching pad for their papers and comments.

Nothing is quite as dampening to the soaring spirits of scholars embarking on an intellectual jamboree as the insistence by some pedant at the outset that one needs to define one's terms. Nevertheless, our discussions have occasionally lacked rigour because of the imprecision of expression and the lack of unanimity with respect to what certain words mean.

One culprit, alas, is the word "science" itself. We very often mean only the hard sciences by it; at other times we include everything that seeks to apply a scientific method, as developed by some of the social sciences. I confess with alacrity to being very much a guilty party here, but that does not rob my comment of its value: the worst people, as has been observed, give the best advice. It might be wise at future conferences to specify the differences in detail and to trace the consequences of the difference for public policy with respect to science. Indeed, we could do a lot worse, at some stage, than to examine the concept and application to our concerns of what has come to be known as the "policy sciences".

A related concern emanates from a different aspect of the appropriate use of words. An understanding and illuminating attack on intellectual problems requires that one ask the appropriate questions. And in most questions there usually lurk unconscious or even biased assumptions which tilt the discourse toward certain normatively inspired directions. For an inquiry to be truly disinterested, it is essential that these latent potentially distorting traps are identified and removed. This can only occur when a conscious and determined effort is made to examine the prior questions and their hidden agendas from as objective a view as possible. The greatest chance of success here results from an examination of the agenda, and its underlying assumptions, by a heterogeneous group of people with divergent disciplinary, and normative backgrounds. It may be a good idea, at future such conferences, to devote at least a portion of the first session to an identification and a fairly specific discussion of the central questions to be pursued in subsequent sessions and to invite an aggressive search for such hidden agendas as may inadvertently have been smuggled into the discourse.

Finally, although it is inevitable that at a symposium discussing statistics, science, public policy and "the two cultures" the topic of education would periodically surface, I have been astounded by the frequency of this occurrence. This theme intruded on our consciousness in several contexts and in numerous forms. It is my impression that this happened much more frequently this year than on previous occasions. But it was, for the most part, marginal or tangential to the main points under discussion. The importance attached to the topic was nevertheless considerable and widely shared. This being the case, we would be wise to bite the bullet and at a future conference, accord it the place of honour on the agenda.

Given the composition of the conference participants, whenever learning and knowledge in science are mentioned, the post-secondary level normally receives privileged attention. The subject is, however, at least equally important in the context of primary and secondary education, as well as in that of life-long learning. If we address education as our principal concern at some time in the future, it should be examined at various levels and at different phases of the human life cycle.

REFERENCE

Wolpert, L. (2000), "Public Understanding of Science", in *Statistics, Science and Public Policy: The Two Cultures?* ed. A.M. Herzberg and I. Krupka, Kingston: Queen's University, pp. 223-225.

APPENDIX

CONFERENCE ON
STATISTICS,
SCIENCE AND
PUBLIC POLICY

21-24 APRIL 1999 THE TWO CULTURES?

Queen's University International Study Centre   Herstmonceux Castle   Hailsham, U.K.

PROGRAMME

WEDNESDAY 21 APRIL

Dinner
18.00 - 19.00

Opening Session
19.30 - 21.00
19.30 Introduction
19.45 P.Calamai *The Toronto Star*
20.30 Discussion

THURSDAY 22 APRIL

A. Beyond the Endless Frontier of Science (Revised)
8.30 - 10.30
8.30 Introduction
8.35 T.A.Brzustowski *Natural Sciences and Engineering Research Council of Canada*
8.50 R.E.Taylor *Stanford Linear Accelerator*
9.05 J.Ziman *Aylesbury, U.K.*
9.20 Discussion

B. Science and the Public Purse
11.00 - 12.30
11.00 Introduction
11.05 P.O.Larsen *The Danish National Research Foundation*
11.20 J.Meisel *Queen's University*
11.35 M.E.Thompson *University of Waterloo*
11.50 Discussion

C. Natural and Social Sciences
14.00 - 15.45
14.00 Introduction
14.05 D.R.Cox *Nuffield College, Oxford*
14.20 T.G.Flynn *Queen's University*
14.35 F.K.Hare *University of Toronto*
14.50 D.B.McLay *Queen's University*
15.05 Discussion

D. Science and Public Policy
16.15 - 18.00
16.15 Introduction
16.20 T.A.Brzustowski *Natural Sciences and Engineering Research Council of Canada*
16.35 J.H.Carey *National Water Research Institute, Canada*
16.50 A.J.Carty *National Research Council of Canada*
17.05 P.Milliken *Member of Parliament, Canada*
17.20 Discussion

Dinner / Concert
19.00 - 21.00

FRIDAY 23 APRIL

E. The Culture of Accountability
8.30 - 10.30
8.30 Introduction
8.35 J.C.Bailar *University of Chicago*
8.50 F.D.Gault *Statistics Canada*
9.05 L.Horlick *University of Saskatchewan*
9.20 G.H.Reynolds *Centers for Disease Control, Atlanta*
9.35 Discussion

F. The Statisticians' Culture
11.00 - 12.30
11.00 Introduction
11.05 S.W.J.Evans *Quintiles, U.K.*
11.20 E.A.Gehan *Georgetown University Medical Center*
11.35 Discussion

G. The Culture of the Media
14.00 - 15.30
14.00 Introduction
14.05 J.C.Bailar *University of Chicago*
14.20 S.Strauss *The Globe and Mail*
14.35 Discussion

H. The University Culture
16.00 - 17.45
16.00 Introduction
16.05 E.B.Andersen *University of Copenhagen*
16.20 R.W.Oldford *University of Waterloo*
16.35 Discussion

Banquet
19.00 - 21.00
L.Wolpert *University College London*

SATURDAY 24 APRIL

I. The Scientists' Rôle
8.30 - 10.15
8.30 Introduction
8.35 P.Campbell *Nature*
8.50 L.Wolpert *University College London*
9.05 Discussion

J. Conclusions and Discussion
10.30 - 12.15
10.30 Introduction
10.35 D.R.Cox *Nuffield College, Oxford*
10.50 J.Meisel *Queen's University*
11.05 Discussion

244

We gratefully acknowledge the following benefactors whose generosity has made this Conference possible:

AIR CANADA

Berry Brothers & Rudd Ltd.

Camera Kingston

Campus Bookstore, Queen's University

Donner Canadian Foundation

Galerie d'Art Vincent, Château Laurier, Ottawa

GlaxoWellcome, U.K.

Some anonymous donors are also gratefully thanked.

CONFERENCE ON STATISTICS, SCIENCE AND PUBLIC POLICY

21-24 APRIL 1999 — THE TWO CULTURES?

Queen's University International Study Centre   Herstmonceux Castle   Hailsham, U.K.

LIST OF PARTICIPANTS

E.B.Andersen *University of Copenhagen*

D.F.Andrews *University of Toronto*

J.C.Bailar *University of Chicago*

A.M.Benidickson *Queen's University*

T.A.Brzustowski *Natural Sciences and Engineering Research Council of Canada*

P. Calamai *The Toronto Star*

P.Campbell *Nature*

J.H.Carey *National Water Research Institute of Canada*

A.J.Carty *National Research Council of Canada*

D.R.Cox *Nuffield College, Oxford*

H.E.Daniels *University of Cambridge*

D.Davis *Canadian High Commission, London*

P.J.Donnelly *University of Oxford*

A.F.Ebbutt *GlaxoWellcome, U.K.*

S.J.W.Evans *Quintiles, U.K.*

B.Farbey *University College London*

T.G.Flynn *Queen's University*

S.Fortier *Queen's University*

C.E.S.Franks *Queen's University*

F.D.Gault *Statistics Canada*

E.A.Gehan *Georgetown University Medical Center*

F.K.Hare *University of Toronto*

A.M.Herzberg *Queen's University*

L.Horlick *University of Saskatchewan*

K.U.Ingold *National Research Council of Canada*

I.Krupka *Public Policy and Management, Ottawa*

P.O.Larsen *The Danish National Resarch Foundation*

P.Luciani *Donner Canadian Foundation*

D.B.McLay *Queen's University*

D.L.McLeish *University of Waterloo*

J.Meisel *Queen's University*

P.Milliken *Member of Parliament, Canada*

R.W.Oldford *University of Waterloo*

G.H.Reynolds *Centers for Disease Control, Atlanta*

V.H.Smith *Queen's University*

A.T.Stewart *Queen's University*

S.Strauss *The Globe and Mail*

R.E.Taylor *Stanford Linear Accelerator*

M.E.Thompson *University of Waterloo*

R.J.Tomkins *University of Regina*

L.Wolpert *University College London*

J.Ziman *Aylesbury, U.K.*